WHAT IS THE ORIGIN OF MAN?

The Answers of Science
and the Holy Scriptures

*An Arabic edition of the present work
is in press*

*By the same author
and publisher*

'LA BIBLE, LE CORAN ET LA SCIENCE'
(THE BIBLE, THE QUR'AN AND SCIENCE)

Ist Edition, 1976
10th Edition, 1983
revised and expanded

TRANSLATIONS AVAILABLE IN:

English
Arabic
Turkish
Serbo-Croat
Indonesian
Urdu
Persian
Gujrati

THE FRENCH, ENGLISH AND ARABIC EDITIONS ARE DISTRIBUTED BY:

INTER-FORUM
13, rue de la Glacière, 75624 Paris Cedex 13

Dr MAURICE BUCAILLE

What is the Origin of Man?

The Answers of Science and the Holy Scriptures

Translated from the French
by Alastair D. Pannell and the Author

Third Edition, revised

PUBLISHER
SEGHERS
6 Place Saint-Sulpice
75006 PARIS

Should you wish to be kept informed of works recently published by Seghers, please write to Les Editions Seghers, Service 'Bulletin', 6, place Saint-Sulpice, 75279 Paris Cedex 06. The publishers will send you free of charge, and with no obligation, an illustrated monthly brochure containing full details of their new books.

© Editions Seghers, 6, place Saint-Sulpice,
75006 PARIS, France.

ISBN Version française : 2-221-00781-6
ISBN Version anglaise : 2-221-01101-5

CONTENTS

III. – THE FIRST ANSWER
OF THE HOLY SCRIPTURES : THE BIBLE

IV. – THE ORIGIN, TRANSFORMATIONS
AND REPRODUCTION OF MAN
ACCORDING TO THE QUR'AN

V. – THE COMPATIBILITY BETWEEN
RELIGION AND SCIENCE

INTRODUCTION

Man has pondered his origins for thousands of years, but until recently, his only source of ideas consisted of notions drawn from religious teachings and various philosophical systems. Not until modern times, and the arrival of data of a different kind, has he been able to approach the problem of his origins from a new angle.

We live in a time where reason and the conquests of science claim to provide logical answers to all the great questions asked by the human intellect. Likewise, the problem of the origin of man has primarily been presented by some as a matter that can be perfectly explained by secular knowledge. Darwin's *On the Origin of Species,* which appeared in England in 1859, enjoyed a great success with the public, and during the years that followed, it became clear just how significant was the effect of a theory which, as far as the origin of man was concerned, did little more than offer suggestions. A basic hostility toward religious teachings already existed, however, and in Darwin's theory, people saw what seemed to be a decisive argument : Through what appeared to be a logical assimilation, they felt free to postulate that man was descended from the apes. This went beyond Darwin's theory, however, for by extrapolation, such people had managed to assert that just as other species must have come from a different, pre-existing species, so man must have appeared on earth as the result of an evolution from a neighbouring lineage in the animal kingdom.

This statement concerning the origins of man came as a profound shock to all those who remained faithful to the teachings of the Bible, for they believed that man was created by God. Moreover, the very idea of the evolution of species contradicted the words of the Bible, which stated quite clearly that the species were fixed and immutable. Secular theory and religious teaching were at odds, and the consequences of this confrontation were far-reaching indeed. It was maintained that the Bible–until that time considered to be the word of God–had been found wrong. Credance could no longer be given to it, and for many, that meant rejection of the entire text of the Bible. As a result, the theory gained ground that scientific data undermined the faith in God.

At first glance, this argument seems logical, but it does not hold water today because when talking of the Biblical texts, we now possess certain facts that were only beginning to be discovered at the end of the nineteenth century. The idea of a text of revelation–to be accepted without questioning a single sentence–gave way to the notion of a text inspired by God. The text of inspiration was written by mortal men at different points in time, it took its cue from ideas of the day, and included the traditions, myths and superstitions prevalent at the time it was written. "The scientific errors in the Bible are the errors of mankind, for long ago man was like a child, as yet ignorant of science." This quotation from the work of the eminent Christian thinker Jean Guitton (1978) leads us to view the texts of the Bible from an angle very different from what was once the rule.

Indeed, the texts referred to here were consistently thought to have been written by Moses himself. In actual fact, however, the longest part of Genesis (the Sacerdotal narrative) was written by priests in the sixth century B.C. There is, however, a second narration, the Yahvist version, that probably dates back to the ninth or tenth century B.C. In view of this, it is difficult to take archaic ideas seriously. I have given a detailed account of this question in 'La Bible, le Coran et la Science' [*The Bible, the Qur'an and Science*] [1], and if we add to it ideas put forward on the texts by Christian exegetes themselves, we may conclude that there is no need to prolong the antagonism between the supremacy of scientific fact and the primacy of Biblical teachings.

Later on, we shall see that the situation is quite different for other Scriptures, on account of their origin as well as their content. Here again, however, the age-old antagonism between religion and science is no longer justified.

Nevertheless, the fact remains that many scientists continue to view with disdain–or at least with indifference–any comment that touches on the supernatural, an attitude which appears to have hardened over the last few decades : Science is the key to everything, and sooner or later it must reveal facts that will enable us to form an

1. Published by Seghers, Paris, 10th edition, 1983. Also available in English from the same publisher.

exact picture of the origins of life, the formation and functioning of living matter, the appearance on earth of organisms ranging from the most basic to the most complex, and last but not least, the origins of man. In view of this, we may well ask whether religious teachings have not been superseded by progress. How indeed can we fail to be impressed by the stupendous discoveries of modern times—particularly in molecular biology and genetics—when these discoveries have enabled us to acquire an astonishingly precise insight into the field of cellular physiology?

It is easy to understand the excitement of researchers. Aware of their immense scope for discovery and action, they have even developed projects concerning the man of the future. In their view, certain of his qualities or characteristics could be 'oriented'–a concept that is today seen as a theoretical possibility. Many scientists researching the practical applications of genetics are undoubtedly appalled at the consequences that might arise if possibilities became realities. All the same, the very fact of wielding such power–if only theoretical power–is surely a source of great excitement for researchers. In the minds of many scientists, the knowledge that such a power exists may lead them to consider that the ability to change living matter according to their fancy–for that is what it comes down to–renders obsolete any theory on the origins of life that incorporates the supernatural. The same applies to those who confidently expect one day to see primary living matter created in the laboratory. Greatly to their credit is the fact that they have contributed data of immense value to our knowledge of life. They are seriously in error, however, when they imagine that from their laboratory–and *only* from their laboratory (along with additional mathematical studies)–have come, or will come, definitive data concerning man and the origins of life.

In actual fact, the subject of man's origins and evolution is extremely complex. It embraces so many disciplines that it is questionable whether a single person could make a detailed confrontation between the great mass of data, hypotheses and judgements that has been formed. Under the circumstances, we cannot fail to be sceptical when we are told that a certain idea drawn from a study limited to a single field provides us with the definitive answer to the question in hand. Clearly, this kind of zeal for an idea that often derives from mere supposition or foregone conclusion is detrimental to our overall knowledge of the subject.

Some researchers seem to be driven by the misguided wish to defend ideologies that have nothing to do with science. This fact is stressed by P.-P. Grassé, who for 30 years held the Chair of

Evolutionary Studies at the Sorbonne, in his recent work entitled 'L'Homme en accusation' [*Man Stands Accused* [1]], in which he is extremely critical of today's neo-Darwinism. In the present work, I shall be citing many of the ideas put forward by this eminent zoologist, for I am convinced that his theories are correct. Grassé concludes that while the fact of evolution is beyond question, there are great gaps in our knowledge of the way it operates, and there is no valid explanation of the factors determining it : The random mutations that take place in the genes which control heredity are insufficient to play a determinant role in evolution itself. In the case of man, a fact such as the development of the brain since the Australopithecus, over a period covering at the very most 80,000 generations, is inconceivable in neo-Darwinian terms. One of the great mysteries of human evolution is the (almost total) loss of man's innate behaviour, a feature that has remained present and active in apes. Man's evolution cannot be compared point for point with that of the rest of the animal kingdom.

In spite of this, we are constantly supplied with inaccurate data to support the opposite theory. Not long ago, for example, I listened to a radio interview with a member of an important research institute. The interview was aired as part of the main news programme of the day and reached hundreds of thousands of listeners. During the interview, the scientist in question–supported by the prestige attached to his position–stated firmly that the relationship between man and the apes had been clearly established by experiments leading to the creation of hybrid genes : A new chemical complex had been constituted at the level of the molecule, made from components taken from both man and apes. While this may be perfectly feasible in theory, it tells us absolutely nothing. The fallacy lies in the fact that the gene was presented as a 'messenger' capable of carrying information, and hence of triggering the creation of new living tissue, a statement for which there is not one jot of evidence. What a pity it is that we live in an age where sensational but erroneous information is more likely to capture the public imagination than carefully weighed judgements expressing reservations and pointing toward the existence of facts as yet unknown.

Perhaps it is enough to remain at this stage, simply devoting our discussion of the origins of man to a review of the facts that modern scientific knowledge allows us to present as certainties or hypotheses, and at the same time refuting ideas that appear incorrect. What,

1. Published by Albin Michel, Paris, 1980.

indeed, is the point of bringing into the discussion the Holy Scriptures of the monotheistic religions?

First let me reply to those who consider their scientific knowledge to be one thing and their religious beliefs to be another–a group that has continued to grow over the past few decades. To the atheist, mention of the supernatural will seem anachronistic, even in cases where science encounters enigmas–the genetic code, for example. The idea of approaching a question such as this in metaphysical terms is unacceptable to the atheist, even though there is little room for any alternative solution. The existence of this separation between science and religious belief is in keeping with the reasoned ways of modern thought. As far as I am concerned, however, the separation provides grounds for a discussion of the reverse theory, one which seems to me to correspond to the reality of the situation. The 'separatists' could just as easily be believers in God who harbour a certain fear that science will raise questions about their religion through a comparison they have often been told is dangerous.

Many other reasons abound, especially lack of understanding. This has often been noted between those of different faiths, who know little of other religions (and often little of their own Scriptures as well). We must bear in mind the fact that the monotheistic religions [1]–chronologically, Judaism, followed by Christianity and then Islam–represent the religious beliefs of over one third of humanity. We cannot overlook these religions, and it is imperative to know how each of them views the origins of man. Particularly interesting is the examination of a religion's approach when seen in the light of what we know today about the origins of the Scriptures specific to each religion. The examination gives rise to new ideas, from which lessons may be drawn that are at present unsuspected by many people.

In the case of the Bible, the information provided on the Biblical authors has modified archaic or obsolete opinions, and has helped us distinguish the human factor in the texts. One of them is short, possibly having been truncated long ago, and it sheds light on what people in the ninth and tenth centuries B.C. thought about the origins of man : This is the Yahvist version of the Creation. The best-known text, the Sacerdotal version, is the work of priests in the sixth century B.C. It is the time-honoured description of the Creation which appears in the first part of Genesis, setting forth the traditions

---

1. I have not studied the ideas on the origins of man expressed in the religions of Asia. The question is not dealt with in any depth by these religions, nor is it treated in the concrete terms we are used to in the West–as far as I know, at least.

of the day. Later on, the Christian religion adopted the Biblical tradition and reproduced in the New Testament data concerning the length of time man had been on earth. For centuries, the data were faithfully repeated in Bibles, and I can remember seeing in 1930 a manual of religious instruction which stated that according to the Bible, man's appearance on earth should be placed at roughly 4,000 B.C. That is the sort of instruction budding young Christians received in my day!

Mistaken ideas regarding the Qur'an have been common in Christian countries for a very long time. They still persist, as far as the history and content of the Qur'an are concerned. Because of this, the data in the Qur'an on the subject of man's origins must be preceded by a description of the way in which the Qur'an was communicated to man. The assertions on the origins of man to be found in the Qur'an will undoubtedly astonish many people, just as they astonished me when I first discovered them. The comparison of the Biblical and Qur'anic texts is moreover highly revealing : Both of them speak of God the Creator, but the scientifically unacceptable detail in the Biblical description of the Creation is absent from the Qur'an. In fact, the Qur'an contains statements concerning man that are astounding : It is impossible to explain their presence in human terms, given the state of knowledge at the time the Qur'an was communicated. In the West, such statements had never before formed the subject of a scientific communication until November 9, 1976, when I presented a paper to the French National Academy of Medicine on the physiological and embryological data present in the Qur'an, roughly fourteen centuries ahead of modern discoveries.

When taken together with Qur'anic statements on other natural phenomena, the details in the Qur'an on the origins of man form an important factor in the age-old debate between science and religion. They reopen the discussion by focusing on new arguments. In view of such significant points of agreement between firmly established scientific data and a Holy Scripture, we must reconsider hasty judgements which have devoted more attention to abstract concepts than facts.

From the nineteenth century onward, religion and science have been set in opposition in the West. The argument in favour of this has been the discrepancy between the Biblical text and scientific data. If we adhere strictly to the facts, however, we shall see that the opposition between the two was totally deprived of meaning from the moment the human origin of the texts in dispute was established. It is important to remember that the authors of the Biblical texts are considered by Christian exegetes themselves to have been inspired by God. All the same, the Biblical authors may have introduced inaccuracies to the text, without in the least betraying their divine inspiration. These inaccuracies could have arisen from the language of the day, or through references to traditions still honoured during the period. In the light of this, the presence of scientific error is hardly surprising. What would be surprising, from a logical point of view, would be the absence of any errors at all. The opinions of modern Christian exegetes on the Biblical texts are now clearly in agreement with the discoveries of science concerning the discrepancy between scientific data and the contents of the texts. According to the document adopted by the Second Vatican Council (1962-1965), the books of the Old Testament contain material that is 'imperfect and obsolete'. Although the document does not actually state which material, in reading this, I do not think we can find a better confirmation of the accuracy of the theory put forward in the present work.

I have every reason to believe that similar opinions prevail in the most enlightened circles of Judaism. I refer in particular to my conversation several years ago with an extremely important figure in the Jewish world, the main subject of which was the Sacerdotal narrative of Genesis. In the course of our meeting, we agreed that the scientific errors in the text could be explained by the fact that the main preoccupation of the priests of the sixth century B.C. was to instruct the faithful on the omnipotence of God. To do this, they related a story traditional at the time describing the origins of the heavens, the earth, living creatures and man. The story was cast in images and words that could be readily understood by the priests' contemporaries. The length of time that has elapsed since man first appeared on earth, as stated in the Hebrew calendar, should also be viewed in this light. Indeed, the statement of Biblical teaching that is most obviously at odds with science is that man first appeared on earth 5,742 years ago (calculated from late 1981). The moment we accept the existence of arguments that prevent us from taking this affirmation at face value, we can no longer use it as a legitimate accusation against the Bible in the confrontation between science and the Scriptures : It must be placed in its human context.

In the case of man, by comparing the Scriptural texts and modern knowledge, it became clear that the data in Genesis referred to here ought to be set apart for the reasons already mentioned. If we accept this, there is no longer any incompatibility betweeen the teachings of the Scriptures and modern scientific discoveries, concerning the general concept of the creation of man and other views on the first stages of humanity. This is undoubtedly an unusual way of introducing the supernatural, but that does not alter its validity or usefulness. This approach avoids appealing to sentimental arguments that rely on people's emotions or their spiritual state–the accusation usually levelled by materialist thinkers at those who tend to offer arguments based on faith.

Why should the idea of God not grow from extremely logical reflection concerning the infinitely large or the infinitely small? The strict order to be seen in both cases is patently obvious to anyone who takes the trouble to find out about them objectively and impartially. Similarly, in the field dealt with in this book, we shall arrive at the idea that there exists an amazing degree of organization in the functioning and evolution of living matter. Needless to say, God does not manifest Himself scientifically, yet it is perfectly possible to conceive of Him in scientific terms. My personal outlook remains profoundly rational, and although I have adopted the conclusions of modern science (when these are firmly established facts and not mere conjectures), I cannot find any incompatibility between scientific findings and Scriptural teachings. At the same time, however, the origin and history of the Scriptural texts must also be taken into consideration. If we omit this aspect, we shall make an uneven assessment of the Scriptures, for we shall have failed to make allowance for the part played by error or human interpretation. I am convinced that such errors of interpretation were the result of lack of information. The present book grew from the conviction that on the extremely sensitive subject of man's origins, a comparison between scientific data and Scriptural teachings might help clarify points too often left obscure. I hope that the discussion of the answers provided by both sources will show that it is time for past antagonisms to disappear.

I

EVOLUTION IN THE ANIMAL KINGDOM : ESTABLISHED FACTS AND THE GAPS IN OUR KNOWLEDGE

THE ORIGINS OF LIFE
AND THE DIVERSITY OF LIVING BEINGS

If we are to believe certain researchers and their statements concerning the phenomenon of life, there are no more secrets left to discover today. "The origins of life no longer form the subject of laboratory investigation", stated an eminent specialist in molecular biology in 1972. Always assuming these words still carry a meaning, we may conclude that life does not contain any facts we do not know. In reality, however, the situation is quite different, and there are plenty of mysteries that still surround the origins of life.

Ingenious experiments have for many years been repeatedly performed by biochemists and biophysicians in an attempt to prove the possibility of spontaneously obtaining infinite quantities of certain chemical compounds found in cells that are structurally highly complex. The scientists in question are of the opinion that due to favourable physical influences, the compounds were able spontaneously to combine together in an organized fashion, and by uniting, were able to produce the fantastic complex we call the cell, or even more rudimentary living organisms. A statement such as this is tantamount to saying that the possibility of spontaneously forming steel particles from iron ore and coal at high temperature could have led to the construction of the Eiffel Tower through a series of happy coincidences that assembled the materials in proper order. Even then, this comparison is very weak, for the actual structural complexity of an elementary living organism is much more complex than the structure of the Eiffel Tower, considered in 1889 to be a triumph of metal construction.

Those who ardently defend the role of chance base their opinions on experiments of this kind, which claim to reproduce the possible origins of life. They repeat the views of Miller, who in 1955 induced the formation of complex chemical compounds, such as the amino acids present in cellular proteins, using electric sparks in an atmosphere of gas composed of steam, methane, ammonia and hydrogen. Needless to say, such experiments do not provide any explanation for the organization of the components; nor do we have any idea whether this favourably composed gas really existed in the earth's atmosphere two or three billion years ago. A theory cannot be built on unknown facts such as these. Even if a gas of this kind did exist in the earth's atmosphere; even if certain physical conditions did trigger high-powered electrical phenomena; even if complex organic chemical compounds had formed as a result of this fortunate combination of circumstances, there is nothing to prove that they could have induced the creation of living matter. The determining factor for this phenomenon remains unknown. Some researchers admit that there is an enigma in this. Others point to chance–a convenient loophole that excuses them from acknowledging their ignorance. We shall come back later to the reasons why it is impossible to explain the phenomenon of life in terms such as these.

We must indeed turn to disciplines other than biochemistry to find the first clues to the problem, and in particular we must look toward paleontology. Certain prehistoric animals and vegetals were not totally destroyed after their death. Their remains lay buried in sedimentary terranes, protected thereby from disintegration, and thus providing us with vestiges of these prehistoric life forms. The state in which the vestiges are found sometimes allows us to draw certain conclusions concerning the morphology and age of these once-living beings [1]. It is in fact possible to gain an immediate idea of their age by establishing the date of the terranes. This can be done by various methods, in particular by radioactive measurements (radiochronology). For terranes that are geologically less ancient, carbon 14 tests are used, while strontium and rubidium tests are employed for older terranes. Having carried out these tests, experts can then determine the age of the specimens under investigation.

Tests such as these lead us to think that living beings existed in a unicellular state roughly one billion years ago [2]. Although it cannot be stated for sure, other forms may have existed before them. P.-P. Grassé, in his book entitled 'Evolution du Vivant' *[The Evolution of Living Organisms]* [3], mentions the discovery of vestiges of much older organisms : for example, the existence of organized life forms

---

1. The material studied by Paleontology is limited to the bones and teeth.
2. The earth is 4.5 billion years old.
3. Published by Albin Michel, Paris, 1973.

roughly 3.2 billion years ago in the rock formations of the Transvaal. These forms could possibly represent tiny bacteria, smaller than 1/10,000 of a millimetre, as well as particles of amino acids. These organisms may have employed amino acids, or possibly proteins contained in the sea... Other micro-organisms may also have been present in the sediments, such as cyanophilous algae containing chlorophyl. The latter is a basic agent in photosynthesis, a process by which complex organic compounds are formed from simple components through the effect of light. Fossilized vegetation resembling algae and filamentous bacteria have been found in more recent rock formations (2.3 billion years old) near the shores of Lake Superior in Canada. The bacteria and certain algae displayed an extremely simple structure, without the well-known differentiated elements of the cells. Similar samples dating back roughly one billion years have been discovered in rock formations in Central Australia. This stage probably gave way to a period in which algae of a different kind displayed a genuine cell structure, with a nucleus and chromosomes containing molecules of desoxyribonucleic acid, D.N.A for short. Many facts about these algae remain unknown, however.

The pluricellular stage was to follow, but "in the animal kingdom, between uni- and pluricellular forms, there was still a hiatus". Two basic notions must be mentioned immediately :

a) the aquatic origins of primitive organisms;

b) the emergence of a growing complexity, passing from one form to another combined with the appearance of new organisms.

This growing complexity is ever-present throughout evolution : We find similar fossilized vegetation at a much more 'recent' period, 500 million years ago. We cannot be certain, of course, that today's bacteria are identical to those said to have appeared on earth as the first living organisms. They may have evolved since then, although bacteria such as Escherichia Coli have indeed remained the same for 250 million years.

Whatever the answer, the origins of life definitely appear to be aquatic. According to today's thinking, it is impossible to conceive of life without water. Any search for traces of life on other planets begins with the question: Has water been present there? On the earth's surface, the combination of certain conditions—including the presence of water—was required for life to exist at all.

The complexity of living matter in those very first organisms is not likely to have been as great as it is in today's cells. Nevertheless, as P.-P. Grassé points out : "In order for life to exist, there must be a production and exchange of energy. This is only physically possible within a system that is heterogeneous and complex. The established facts at the command of the biologist provide a reason for him to concede that the first living form was of necessity an organized entity". This leads Grassé to stress the important fact that today's bacteria, which appear to be the simplest living organisms, obviously attain a high degree of complexity. They are indeed composed of thousands of different molecules containing systems of catalysis that are themselves highly numerous, and which enable the bacteria to synthesize their own substance, to grow and to reproduce. The catalysis relies on enzymes, which act in infinitely small quantities, each enzyme performing its own specific function.

Like the amoeba, unicellular life forms are composed of differenciated elements. Their structure is amazingly complex, even though the cells are measured in units of $1/1,000$ of a millimeter. Within the fundamental substance of unicellular forms, called cytoplasm, whose chemical structure is highly complex, there are numerous differentiated elements, the most important of which is the nucleus. This is composed of many parts, in particular the chromosomes containing the genes. These control every single aspect of the cell's functioning. They give orders through a system of information transfer, using transmitters and a system to receive the orders as they come in. The chemical vehicle supporting the genes has been clearly identified : It is desoxyribonucleic acid (D.N.A.), a molecule of complex structure. The 'messenger' is a related molecule known as ribonucleic acid, R.N.A for short. Within the cell, it is this system that ensures the formation of new proteins from simpler chemical elements (synthesis of proteins).

It is difficult not to feel tremendous admiration for the molecular biologists who first discovered these extremely complex mechanisms—systems so perfectly regulated to maintain life that the slightest malfunction leads to deformities or monstrous growths (cancer is a case in point) and ends in death. As far as I am concerned, however, the brilliant analysis of the way this system works (for each and every cell is a kind of computer comprised of innumerable interrelations) is just as amazing as the general conclusions cited above concerning the supposed resolution of unexplained facts on the origins of life. One very important question immediately springs to mind, based on the results of these investigations : How could a system as complex as this have been formed? Was it the work of chance, following a host of trials and errors? That seems most unlikely. What other logical theories are there? It is common knowledge that a computer will only function if it has been programmed, a fact that implies the existence of a *programming intellect, that provides the information required to operate the system.* That is the problem facing all thinking people who seek an explanation to such questions; people who refuse to accept mere words or groundless theories; people who will only acknowledge conclusions based on facts. Given the present state of knowledge, however, science has not provided any answer to this precise point.

The Diversity of Living Beings

There is tremendous diversity among living beings. From the most ancient times, human observers have noted this diversity and have taken great pains to analyse it in minute detail. Naturalists record the striking precision of certain primitive peoples in their ability to distinguish between the species of animals surrounding them. Having received no instruction from outside, these peoples have compiled inventories that are not far off the work of an expert.

The first distinction to be made between living beings is the separation of the animal and vegetable kingdoms. Although they share a common basic element—the cell—as well as numerous constituant substances, they are different in several ways. The vegetable kingdom is directly dependent on the earth for its nourishment. It also requires a much greater capacity for producing complex chemical compounds from simple bodies and light. The animal kingdom, on the other hand, depends on the vegetable kingdom for its nourishment (at least with regard to animals that have attained a certain degree of complexity), and carnivores depend on other species of animal.

Henceforth, we shall concentrate uniquely on the animal kingdom, which is extraordinarily varied and large. There may be as many as 1.5 million species living on our planet. The list has continued to grow, especially in recent decades, with the discoveries made in the marine world. Ever since the natural sciences gained stature and importance in the seventeenth century, formal classifications have constantly appeared, each updated in turn as new data are discovered.

Aristotle drew a distinction between animals with red blood and those without, but no other studies of a serious nature were undertaken until the seventeenth century, when more interesting characteristics began to attract attention. For example, some observers were struck by the question of respiration through the lungs or the branchiae (fish gills), the existence or absence of a vertebral skeleton (backbone), the anatomy of the heart (number of ventricles), or the existence of hair as opposed to feathers. In the classifications that were to follow, characteristics such as these remained distinctive of certain animal groups.

The distribution of distinguishing attributes opened the way for classification by group, with series of subdivisions. Thus the phyla [1] characterise the broad basic divisions of the living beings presenting similar features, allowing us to put them in the same group. Each phylum can be divided into clearly defined classes; these are also determined by a certain number of specific characteristics. Similarly, each class contains several clearly differenciated orders which nevertheless maintain the general features of their class and phylum. An order consists of various families, the families are composed of genera [2], and the genera contain different species displaying both collective and specific characteristics. Classification is further complicated, however, by the existence of intermediary forms.

The first phylum of this classification is composed of unicellular forms, known as protozoans. It includes the most primitive beings, which very probably divided at some point in time, thus giving birth to pluricellular forms : This is the first example of evolution in the course of time.

The structure of these pluricellular forms (spongiae, cnidariae and ctenophores) became more complex as some acquired more specialized functions, without however constituting organs with clearly defined attributes. For example, some provided the covering of animals, others developed the ability to contract, or became sensitive to outside stimuli, others acquired reproductory functions. The system grew more involved when a cavity appeared that served as a digestive tract (cnidariae and ctenophores) and the sensory organs made their appearance. This group did not as yet possess a head, however.

Embryological data have been of great value in establishing the various classifications in the animal kingdom. Thus an important stage in the growth of a structural complexity was reached with the early appearance during embryonic development of an extra germ layer. The number of layers thus grew from two to three, each layer ensuring the formation of clearly defined organs. Animals with three germ layers were in turn divided into 2 groups : those containing a single cavity (the digestive tract) and those with cavities that developed next to the digestive tract and which were responsible for the formation of tissues and various other organs. The broad

1. Plural of phylum.
2. Plural of genus.

divisions of the animal kingdom, here reduced to their most basic terms, already seem to suggest a methodical organization.

The latter guided the birth of the various phyla, of which 20 emerged (very unevenly) into the following four groups :

a) the unicellular forms, constituting a unique phylum;

b) the pluricellular beings containing two germ layers in the embryo [1], these gave birth to three phyla;

c) the pluricellular beings with three germ layers [2] but containing only one cavity, these accounted for six phyla;

d) the group of animals with three germ layers and several cavities, constituting the other twelve phyla, two of which are particularly important : They are the arthropods—which comprise the largest number of species in the animal kingdom, among which we find the insects—and the vertebrates, the latter including fishes, reptiles, birds and mammals.

Nevertheless, the gaps in our knowledge of the transitions from one of these groups to another are very wide indeed. In the case of the insects, one of the most important groups, we know nothing whatsoever of their origins (P.-P. Grassé.) Likewise, there are no fossils left to indicate the beginnings of the various phyla. "Every explanation of the mechanism that governs the creative evolution of the basic organizational plans is weighed down with hypotheses. This statement should figure at the beginning of any book dealing with evolution. Since we have no firm documentary evidence, statements on the origins of the phyla can only be suppositions, opinions whose degree of feasibility we have no way of measuring." P.-P. Grassé's observation on the phyla should caution any statement on the origins of the major basic divisions. From this point of view, the determining causes of the phenomena in question are just as mysterious as the birth of the most rudimentary life forms.

1. The external layer (ectoderm) and the internal layer (endoderm.).
2. The first two layers plus a third (mesoderm) interposed between the two others.

THE CONCEPT OF EVOLUTION
IN THE ANIMAL KINGDOM
THE DIFFICULTY OF SOLVING THE PROBLEM

It is difficult to say at what period prior to the nineteenth century the question of evolution in the animal kingdom was first raised. In the centuries before Christ, several Greek philosophers had already perceived that the living world was subject to transformations. Observers coming after them sometimes displayed startling flashes of intuitive insight. Inevitably, however, their conclusions arose from philosophical ideas or pure speculations. The fact that they later proved to be correct, although the product of sheer guesswork, does not lend any particular value to these early philosophical concepts. Indeed, we should always bear in mind that during the same period, the same philosophers maintained totally inaccurate theories with complete equanimity : the theories concerning the existence of the universe in an identical state throughout eternity, for example.

In 1801, however, Lamarck became the very first naturalist to put forward the idea of evolution. It appeared in his 'Discours d'ouverture' *[Inaugural Speech]*, eight years ahead of his 'Philosophie zoologique' *[Zoological Philosophy]*. For the rest of his life, Lamarck collected arguments to support his theory. Cuvier, the other famous French naturalist of the nineteenth century, published his 'Histoire des ossements fossiles' *[History of Fossilized Bones]* in 1812. He compares present-day animals with fossilized remains, demonstrating the existence of extinct species. Cuvier's study does not, however, support the idea of evolution. J.-P. Lehmann suggests the following reason for this : Cuvier thought that the fossils in question could not be older than the maximum figure of several millenia allotted by the Bible to the earth and the animal kingdom. Because, for example, the Egyptian mummy of an ibis did not indicate that a change had taken place in today's animal, evolution did not exist. In 1859, Darwin introduced the idea of the natural selection of species, and it was not long before others attributed to Darwin's theory the general concept of evolution. J. Roger has indeed pointed out that "the actual word 'evolution' is not part of Darwin's original terminology. It did not appear until the sixth edition of *On the Origin of Species,* and even then it was used more as a general denial of the fixity of the created species than an affirmation of Darwinian transformism proper." Hence, if we are to follow the theories of P.-P. Grassé in 'L'homme en accusation' *[Man Stands Accused]* and of J. Roger, we shall see that the true father of evolution is Lamarck (even though his name is always associated with transformism), while Darwin is little more than a transformist (even though he has always been considered the first naturalist firmly to introduce the idea of evolution.) Later on, we shall take a closer look at the ideas of both Lamarck and Darwin.

However that may be, the data provided by zoology and paleontology combined clearly furnished firm arguments from which to approach the question at issue. Zoology strove to classify the different groups of orders, families, genera and species, basing its distinctions mainly on anatomy, physiology, and embryology. Paleontology, on the other hand, ascertained (or tried to ascertain) at what periods in time life forms appeared similar to those of today, and at what periods beings now extinct first appeared then disappeared. This is an important concept to remember, otherwise we run the risk of misinterpreting the information provided by paleontology : For example, the discovery of certain fossil specimens in terranes dating from a precise geological age does not necessarily mean that these life forms were inexistent before or after the age in question. Errors of this kind are less likely to occur when fossilized forms are highly numerous within a certain period, especially when there are no specimens to be found in fossils pre- or postdating the specific period. In the case of man, however, whenever there are very few genuine–or supposedly genuine–remains, and whenever such vestiges are limited to bone fragments, the way is open for a host of errors, as we shall see later on.

In spite of these reservations, we can derive many ideas from observing how a clearly defined anatomical form present at a certain point in time has succeeded a similar form with a less developed morphology existing in older terranes. This change over a period of time may possibly reflect a better adaptation to what may well have been new conditions of life. Observations such as these must, however, be repeated with many different examples before one can seriously talk of evolution. Only paleontology can provide us with proof of this kind. Having started promisingly in the early nineteenth century, paleontology really came into its own after Darwin. The English naturalist did not employ any decisive arguments from paleontology : In most cases, his opinions rested on the study of *present-day* animals, suggesting an apparent natural selection that did not, however, explain everything. Thus, Darwin's arguments are by no means conclusive.

What can we say today about the definite—or extremely probable—data of paleontology when combined with facts drawn from our knowledge of zoology?

As we have already seen, pluricellular life forms most probably developed from unicellular forms. The most primitive pluricellular beings are likely to have been the spongiae (sponges), which although not possessing clearly differentiated organs already display a reproductive organization that is sexual. From these primitive forms probably derive the cnidariae and ctenophores mentioned earlier. The latter possess the rudiments of organs and cells that have acquired nervous and muscular functions : They are likely to have been formed less than one billion years ago. The first invertebrates probably appeared 500 or 600 million years ago, along with molluscs, annulated worms, and the first insects. The vertebrates came later, roughly 450 million years ago, and likewise certain fishes which continued to develop thereafter. The first terrestrial vertebrates (amphibians and reptiles) appeared some 350 million years ago, and following them came the mammals (180 million years ago) and the birds (135 million years ago). Life forms not only appeared however, they also disappeared, sometimes in very large quantities. The reptiles provide an example of this phenomenon : Having predominated for 200 million years, they went into decline, so that today we have few vestiges to account for reptile life over the past 60 or 70 million years. Their 'place', if one may call it that, has been taken by the mammals.

This deliberately brief and generalized survey shows the magnitude of the evolution toward ever more developed and complex forms. Also evident is the extent to which forms could disappear (and not just the reptiles), thus bringing considerable changes to the general aspect of the living world. Finally, we must mention forms that have remained unchanged for hundreds of millions of years : cockroaches, to take an example from the insect world. There are, however, many other groups to which we shall later return. Each and every one of these data raises considerable problems, thus indicating the complexity of evolution. We are forced to account not only for progressions and regressions, but also for extinctions.

In view of this, the problem of the general evolution of life forms is fantastically vast and complex. It requires us to search into extremely diverse fields : the natural sciences (botany and zoology), comparative anatomy, paleontology, embryology, and chemistry—to mention only those that seem to have provided the most evidence. There are, however, many evolutionary studies published by researchers who, though undoubtedly extremely well-informed in their fields, have an unfortunate tendency to draw generalized conclusions without any detailed knowledge of what experts from other fields have to say on the same subject.

The matter at hand is indeed so vast that very few specialists are able to master each and every aspect of it : To do so would require tremendous experience, as well as knowledge spanning a whole range of different disciplines. It is for this reason that the observer—who by definition is willing to accept any proposition providing it is supported by solid arguments—remains very sceptical of conclusions too heavily based on data from a single field of study. Thus it is difficult to accept certain theories, based on molecular biology or mathematical research in genetics concerning the evolution of living forms, when the authors of these theories quite obviously attach very little importance to the work of their colleagues in other branches of knowledge. For example, what about the work of researchers in the field of paleontology excavating ancient fossilized forms? What about the wealth of relevant facts supplied by comparative anatomy and embryology? Sadly, we must note that specialists in the basic sciences, preoccupied as they are with the origins of life, the beginnings of man and the evolution of living forms, have lost their appetite for arguments based on solid facts from the past.

This criticism is in no way intended to undermine the tremendous value of evolutionary data gleaned from the cell. It is simply aimed at the overly exclusive use of these data, devoid of any interpretation. Unfortunately, this shortcoming is very common nowadays. So many problems containing countless facets are examined by specialists from a wide range of disciplines, only to be viewed in the light that is most congenial to the eyes of the specialists in question. A further difficulty is the frequent and unfortunate intervention of ulterior motives of a religious or metaphysical kind, that quite obviously underlie the opinions of many researchers. For example, a theorist may rely heavily on a material argument, glad to have discovered it if he thinks the argument will support his cherished materialistic theory. But those who are not informed may think it is dangerous to acknowledge the idea of evolution, even in the animal kingdom, for fear that by extending this view to man, they may go against the religious teachings they wish to uphold. In so doing, they are unaware of the fact that certain aspects of modern discoveries that are usually employed to support materialistic views may indeed offer a solid argument to those of diametrically opposed opinions. All of which is to say, that questions of this kind ought to be approached without any preconceived ideas at all.

LAMARCK AND TRANSFORMISM

Nowadays, there is a colossal quantity of data at the disposal of the specialists who seek an answer to the questions raised here. In the past, however, the material available for constructing a theory was very limited indeed. The opinions expressed were strongly influenced by philosophical ideas and religious beliefs. In spite of this however, certain ideas did escape these influences, and in view of the concepts prevalent at the time, they were absolutely revolutionary.

In the sixth century B.C., Anaximander of Miletus put forward the notion of evolution in the animal kingdom. His theory appeared at the time the so-called Sacerdotal version of Genesis was being written on the other side of the Mediterranean, in which there is mention of the creation of living beings 'each according to its kind'. In the century after, Empedocles appears to have sided with the general concept of evolution. He does not, however, seem able to have produced anything but a bizarre account of the origins of man that is entirely the work of his vivid imagination. Lucretius, on the other hand, expresses ideas in his work 'De Natura Rerum' *[On Nature]* that favour the notion of a process of natural selection that preserves the strongest species and eliminates the weakest.

The Bible was responsible for the widespread notion that the species were fixed and unchanging, a concept that held sway until the nineteenth century. Even so, Saint Augustine and several other Fathers of the Church mention certain possibilities of transformation as a result of the potential attributes that God bestowed on the world when He created it.

Buffon was the first thinker to uphold the idea of evolution, but he did so with a certain amount of timidity. Initially, he had considered the species to be fixed and unchanging, but as he grew older and his knowledge of nature increased, he came to view them as in a state of evolution. To be precise, however, he considered the families of animals to have come from a single species, having acquired various characterictics in the course of time while remaining within a certain biological framework. The fact is, he was not prepared to admit that one species could transform itself into another; he only accepted the existence of limited variations. For Buffon, conditions of life—climate, food, domestication—were the prime factors in the changes that took place in animals. His doubts and hesitations are mentioned in P.-P. Grassé's book 'Biologie Animale' *[Animal Biology]* [1] : "Buffon's work gives the impression that the naturalist did not want to follow his thoughts through to the very end. Anxious to preserve his peace and quiet, he was afraid of coming into violent conflict with the preconceived ideas of his day. When the Sorbonne sharply called him back into line, he agreed to everything they asked."

Lamarck, on the other hand, enjoyed a far greater freedom to say what he liked.

Lamarck, the Father of Evolution

Although Lamarck had been the official Botanist to the French king, when the Revolution broke out, he was lucky enough to secure himself a position where he could study and teach without hindrance. Thus, in 1794, he occupied a teaching post at the Muséum National d'Histoire Naturelle [French National Museum of Natural History]. Seven years later, in 1801, he outlined the theory of evolution in his 'Discours d'ouverture du 21 Floréal An 8' *[Inaugural Speech of the 21st. Day of Floreal, Year 8]* [2] —several years before his masterwork 'La Philosophie zoologique' *[Zoological Philosophy]*, which appeared in 1809. Until his dying day, Lamarck worked tirelessly, amassing copious evidence to support his theories. Although they are open to criticism—on certain points his opinions are unacceptable today—they nevertheless represent a step forward so enormous, that there is every reason to call Lamarck the 'Father of Evolution'. But for all this, he died in dreadful intellectual isolation; criticized and mocked by his contemporaries, misjudged and underestimated, in spite of the importance of his work as a naturalist.

Lamarck had shown the "relative unchangeability" of species, which are "only temporarily invariable." If their conditions of life changed, Lamarck considered that the species would change in

1. Co-authors M. Aron and P.-P. Grassé, published by Masson, Paris, 1935.
2. According to the Revolutionary calendar.

"size, form, proportion between their various parts, colour, firmness, agility and industriousness... Changes in their environment modify their needs or create new ones; new habits lead to greater use of certain organs and the neglect of others. When an organ is left unused, it shrinks and may finally disappear altogether". (I owe to P.-P. Grassé this synopsis of Lamarck's ideas on the influence of environment.)

Indeed, it has been observed that the teeth of animals that do not chew their food (the anteater or the whale, for example) tend to atrophy or not to emerge at all. Another example is the mole, whose eyes are so tiny they often see absolutely nothing. Going in the opposite direction, intense use of an organ leads to its development : The feet of birds that live in water become webbed as a result of swimming, the tongue of the anteater grows longer as a result of the way it extends its tongue to catch and coat its victims with a sticky substance. The study of these variations led Lamarck to conclude that when a change occurred, it was toward a more complex organ (in the case of organs that develop as a result of intensive use), and that variations of this kind were transmitted by heredity.

Critical Assessment of Lamarck's Theories

In criticizing Lamarck's theories, one must bear in mind the nature of the data on which, in his day, Lamarck was able to base his ideas. While there are undoubtedly points that he treats somewhat superficially, his ideas nevertheless contain an element of truth. In Lamarck's eyes, the evidence was so striking that in an age where such evidence was denied by others, the truth had to be proclaimed. All the same, Lamarck overestimated the influence of environment, and his idea that characteristics are automatically transferred by heredity is no longer acceptable.

Zoologists have indeed pointed to the existence of changes that were induced by environment–the influence of food on the digestive tract, for example. It is a well-known fact, however, that overworked muscles become hypertrophiated. Similarly, when a duplicate organ is removed, the remaining organ is quite likely to grow bigger, although it does not change at all from a structural point of view. At issue is the usefulness to the individual of the change thus created, a point that has not been proven in the least. Nor is the change definitive within the history of the species, for the hereditary nature of acquired characteristics is a purely intellectual notion. Tests carried out after a change of environment have shown that new characteristics are not passed on to descendants. This is the sharpest criticism to be made of Lamarck's theory. Nevertheless, Lamarck did indeed show the existence of a kind of evolution in the animal kingdom : Where he went wrong was in his assessment of the amplitude of evolution, as gauged through his observations. The explanation he provided was unconvincing, and thus Lamarck was unable to gain acceptance for his ideas. He was vigorously challenged by Cuvier, who favoured the concept of the fixity of species, and it was Cuvier and those of his opinion who won the day.

Lamarck's ideas did not come into favour until several decades after his death, when paleontologists produced evidence–lacking while Lamarck was alive–of morphological changes due to variations in environment. Moreover, the phrase 'influence of the environment' needs to be better understood, for we seem here to be faced with a question of terminology requiring explanation. If by 'environment' we mean all the influences that are likely to produce an effect on living organisms, then quite obviously changes may occur under such conditions. Not all of Lamarck's theories are to be disguarded.

DARWIN AND NATURAL SELECTION,
OR A HYPOTHESIS SURVIVES
THROUGH IDEOLOGY

In order to establish his doctrine, some fifty years after Lamarck, Darwin advanced many more seemingly significant facts than his predecessor. Unfortunately, however, Darwin thought everything could be explained through the postulate of the all-pervading power of natural selection. There is no doubt, moreover, that Darwin was strongly motivated by sociological considerations, factors which should have no place in a scientific doctrine, and yet his work is still very well known today. The following reasons may account for his continuing fame : Darwin's arguments are extremely cleverly presented, and often subtlety is more effective than the rigorousness of the arguments themselves. Nor should we overlook the satisfaction of certain scientists who were quick to use Darwin's theory to discredit Biblical teachings on the subject of the origins of man and the fixity of species. Indeed, with regard to the evolution of species, Darwin's theory was used to prove that man was descended from the great apes. In fact, however, the animalistic origin of man is an idea that was first put forward by Haeckel in 1868.

It is quite common today for people to confuse Darwinism with evolution–a misconception that is extremely annoying because it is totally wrong. Darwin himself presented his theory in quite a different way, as the following extract from *On the Origin of Species* [1] shows :

"Hence, as more individuals are produced than can possibly

---

1. The full title reads *On The Origin Of Species By Means Of Natural Selection Or The Preservation Of Favoured Races In The Struggle For Life.* London, 1859. The texts quoted here are taken from the Pelican Classics Edition, published by Penguin Books, 1981.

survive, there must in every case be a struggle for existence, either one individual with another of the same species, or with the individuals of distinct species, or with the physical conditions of life... Can it, then, be thought improbable, seing that variations useful to man have undoubtedly occurred, that other variations useful in some way to each being in the great and complex battle of life, should sometimes occur in the course of thousands of generations? If such do occur, can we doubt (remembering that many more individuals are born than can possibly survive) that individuals having any advantage, however slight, over others, would have the best chance of surviving and of procreating their kind? On the other hand, we may feel sure that any variation in the least degree injurious would be rigidly destroyed. This preservation of favourable variations and the rejection of injurious variations, I call Natural Selection."

In actual fact, Darwin indicated that he intended to put forward a theory on the origin of species by means of natural selection or the preservation of favoured races in the struggle for life. This became the banner of the evolutionists, which they brandished in the fight between materialistic philosophy and religious faith. The same banner is still being waved today in the same spirit. Darwin has remained one of the idols of the atheistic arsenal, always ready to support whatever ideas bring grist to their mill. As the reader of the present book will see in chapter after chapter, the existence of evolution, even when applied to the human species, no longer constitutes an argument that undermines religious faith. Indeed, the latest studies of biological processes within the cell reveal facts that are significant in a different way from the flimsily based questions which once formed the subject of discussion. They raised points concerning the organization of life and in fact lead us in a direction totally opposite to the main subject of past controversies.

All in all, Darwin's doctrine is very straightforward. He notes the obvious fact that there is a wide variety in the number of characteristics present in individuals belonging to a particular species, and he provides reasons for this that are fairly similar to those of Lamarck. Darwin states that the reproductive cells are modified as well, and that newly acquired attributes are hereditary. He goes further than Lamarck, however, when he talks of the advantages derived from certain modifications that nature, by means of selection, perpetuates through the elimination of the weakest in favour of those most able to survive this pitiless process. According to Darwin, there is also a process of sexual selection in which the females choose the strongest males...

The concept of natural selection exercised a tremendous fascination, and even today, the followers of Darwin consider the advocate of natural selection to be the greatest genius who ever worked in the field of natural sciences. He still remains one of the most venerated zoologists. The highest honours were accorded to him at his death. Although his work had provided arguments to support atheism in the confrontation between religion and science that raged in the second half of the nineteenth century, his mortal remains were interred by the British nation in Westminster Abbey, London.

In actual fact, Darwin's work contains two aspects: The first is scientific, but in spite of the impressive quantity of data observed by Darwin, when all is said and done, the scientific aspect is far from solid; while his observations are extremely interesting from the point of view of the various species, they do not tell us very much about evolution itself–and that is quite a different matter. The second aspect, which is philosophical, is very strongly stressed by Darwin and very clearly expressed.

The Ideas of Malthus as Applied to the Animal Kingdom

Darwin does not hide the influence of Malthus' ideas on his own concept of natural selection. The following quotation from Darwin is taken from P.-P. Grassé's work 'L'homme en accusation' *[Man Stands Accused]*: "In the next chapter the Struggle for Existence amongst all organic beings throughout the world, which inevitably follows from their high geometrical powers of increase, will be treated of. This is the doctrine of Malthus, applied to the whole animal and vegetable kingdoms." This statement appears in the introduction to the second edition of *On the Origin of Species*, 1860.

Before applying a socio-economic theory to data observed in the animal kingdom–a field that by definition has nothing to do with socio-economic theory–, Darwin had indeed pursued very logically his thoughts concerning the natural phenomena he had so carefully observed. From 1831 to 1836, he accompanied the mission of the ship the *Beagle* in the South Atlantic and the Pacific, serving as a naturalist. The voyage provided Darwin with ample opportunity to observe on land. Thus he was struck by the modifications displayed in the species studied, corresponding to the places in which they lived. From this he derived the notion of an absence of fixity, and he compared this to the selective breeding of domestic animals by humans in an effort to improve the various species. The question that sprang to his mind was : How could selection be applied to organisms living in their natural state? By this I think what he probably meant was : Do the factors that man uses when making his selections for the purpose of cross-breeding animals possess an equivalent in nature? There does indeed seem to be spontaneous selection between animals in their natural state. Thus a question was raised and a hypothesis suggested, but in the answer that followed there was no certainty whatsoever.

It is very difficult to understand how Darwin could have found justification for this theory in the ideas put forward by Malthus. The latter was an Anglican clergyman whose initial interest was in demographic factors and their economic consequences. In 1798, he anonymously published an *Essay on the Principle of Population* in which he proposed various solutions. Some of them are totally inhuman, such as the famous Poor Law, which abolished assistance to those who produced nothing and lived off the rich. As far as Malthus was concerned, selection operated among human beings : *Only those most able to produce deserved to survive,* those less favoured by nature were destined to disappear. In view of the dreadful misery present among the working classes at this early stage in the industrial revolution, such total lack of basic human charity is staggering. Darwin saw interesting ideas in the propositions of Malthus, and he applied to human beings the hypothesis of a selective process that ensured the survival of the fittest and most able at the expense of the weak–a selection that nature itself would operate.

Those are the facts, and if Darwin's statement were not there, written in black and white, who would ever think of associating his early ideas with the pitilessly rigid prescriptions of Malthus? In 'L'homme en accusation' *[Man Stands Accused],* P.-P. Grassé is extremely critical of Darwin for having drawn his inspiration from Malthus and for the unfortunate influence he created :

"Due to its basic precepts and final conclusions, Darwinism is the most antireligious and most materialistic doctrine in existence." P.-P. Grassé is amazed that Christian men of science do not seem to be aware of this. He goes on to note that "Karl Marx was much more perceptive. When he read *On the Origin of Species,* he recognized the materialistic, atheistic inspiration of the work. That is why he admired it so much and why he used it in the way he did. In its pages, Marx found the material needed to dissolve all religious belief, an opinion shared by the founders of the Soviet Union, especially Lenin... They created a Museum of Darwinism in Moscow in order to combat 'Christian obscurantism' with the help of scientific data!"

Criticism of Darwin's Theory

It is patently clear that if left to themselves, animals or plants that contain a defect or infirmity will be the first to disappear. There is little need to cite examples supporting this statement of the obvious. But to go from this to saying that selection in nature ensures only the survival of the strongest and fittest is quite a different matter. Our response must be much more subtle.

When we observe animal populations living within a certain territory, we are well aware that a system of balances is in operation, even though the balances may not be the same everywhere–in one section of the territory a species predominates, in another it is supplanted by a different species. In cases such as this, there is no doubt that selection is operating within a single population, but it does not influence biological evolution as a whole.

Observations are further distorted by the arrival of cataclysms or extreme changes in climate over the ages. Such events may affect vast areas, striking blindly, and without any of the selective influences one might expect to find in the disappearance of a population : Flooding from rivers or the sea, or fires for example, can cause great devastation, but that does not mean that their victims were specially selected. Likewise during the various geological eras, glaciations struck indiscriminately.

An objection to Darwin's theory that P.-P. Grassé raises is the fact that death does not always make a distinction. It does not always kill the weakest and preserve the strongest, as Darwin would like us to think. P.-P. Grassé gives precise examples of cases where it is not possible to know, at a certain stage in the metamorphosis of living beings, why it is that one batch evolves normally and another does not. When animals fight, it is not always the strongest and best equipped who win the battle : The percentage of animals who are victorious depends on factors such as chance and circumstance. The idea of sexual selection is also open to considerable criticism : It is very unrealistic to imagine that the female always chooses the strongest male, for the element of chance in such encounters outweighs individual preferences.

What evidence is there of the power of selection to provoke the emergence of new forms? Darwin likened natural selection to the artificial selection practised by man. In actual fact, however, artificial selection does not create new species; all it does is influence certain characteristics. The individuals themselves do not 'take leave' of their species, as it were. Artificial selection does not trigger the formation of new organs, it does not lead to the creation of a new genus, nor does it engender a new type of organization. These facts are very clearly stated by P.-P. Grassé who cites the example of colon bacillus and drosophila, organisms which can undergo mutations while preserving the characteristics of their species that have been passed down for millions of years. Thus the minor individual variations mentioned by Darwin are by no means hereditary–a point on which Darwin's theory is just as open to criticism as Lamarck's.

Data on Evolution in the Animal Kingdom that Contradict Darwinian Concepts

In this section, we shall quote the objections raised by P.-P. Grassé, the first of which is Darwin's own admission that his doctrine was incomplete : "Judging from letters (and I have just seen one from Thwaites to Hooker), and from remarks, the most serious omission in my book was not explaining how it is, as I believe, that all forms do not necessarily advance, how there can be simple organisms still existing..." (Letter to Asa Gray, May 22, 1860, from *The Life and Letters of Charles Darwin,* by Francis Darwin, 3 vols, published by John Murray, 1887.)

Darwin speaks of the 'progress' that natural selection ought to ensure in living beings, by which he confuses 'progress' with growing organizational complexity, an essential aspect of evolution to which we shall return. Elsewhere, he expresses his amazement at the existence of living forms which have not changed at all over the course of time but have remained at the stage of very simple organisms : This is a phenomenon that is easily explained today in terms of modern ideas on mutagenesis. Every living being is affected by mutagenesis, minor variations which do not, however, cause the organisms concerned to leave the framework of their species.

For example, zoologists are very familiar with the so-called 'panchronic' species, which have remained the same throughout the course of time. Blue algae are a case in point : There is every reason to think that these organisms have been in existence for at least one billion years, and yet they are still the same today. Other examples are the ferro-bacteria, sponges, molluscs, and animals such as the opossum or the famous coelacanth which, though hundreds of millions of years old, have not changed at all. The coelacanth caused great excitement when it was discovered off the coast of South Africa in 1938. It is a fish, over 4 1/2 feet long, that is thought to have appeared roughly 300 millions years ago. Several other examples of this fish have been caught in more recent times–almost to order, for the local fishermen are familiar with the coelacanth. Examination of these fish provided important information on the anatomy and physiology of a species which, like so many others, refused to conform to the natural selection put forward by Darwin. At the same time however, none of these organisms has ceased to undergo mutations–a process that is inevitable. As far as the fish are concerned, however, their evolution has come to an end. If we seek the reason why, we find that Darwin's theory is unable to provide an answer that both agrees with his doctrine and explains the preservation of these hereditary characteristics.

According to the law of natural selection, such imperfections as the excessive development of a single characteristic should not be allowed to develop and perpetuate themselves to the extent that they harm the animal or vegetal concerned. Nevertheless, it is a well-known fact that certain conifer plants produce chemical compounds that irresistably attract coleoptera which then devour them. The production of these chemical compounds is therefore responsible for the death of the plant. This process has been going on for millions of years : Natural selection does not intervene to save pine and fir trees from destruction by insects.

Similarly, the antelope is able to escape its enemies by its extreme speed, and yet there are species of this animal whose hooves contain glands that secrete a particular odour which, as the antelope runs, is left on the ground. All the attacking carnivore has to do is follow the scent in order to track down its prey. Thus the graceful antelope is left unprotected by the theories of Darwin! Another example of a harmful individual attribute is the excessive growth of horns, which can constitute a handicap. Finally, we are all familiar with the case of the deer, whose antlers impede its movement through the forest.

Studies of the coelacanth have shown the extent to which this fish contains characteristics that are paradoxical to the zoologist. If natural selection were genuinely present, these characteristics ought by rights to have disappeared, thus providing the coelacanth with a more functional morphology. The fact is, however, nothing has changed for several hundred million years.

If we examine the argument put forward by zoological specialists who are opposed to Darwinism, we shall undoubtedly see that it is sometimes quite difficult to distinguish between a harmful and a beneficial morphological change in an animal. For example, snakes have lost all their limbs, but that does not mean they have been placed in an inferior state. Given a case such as this, what right have we to speak of an animal that has 'regressed'? The example of the snake is indeed extremely revealing, for the loss of its limbs was accompanied by other major modifications of its skeleton and numerous viscera, affecting its general anatomy. Zoologists are at a loss to explain in Darwinian terms such sweeping changes; they are modifications which were perfectly coordinated over the course of time, and the succession of phenomena here appears infinitely complex, from an anatomical point of view. Thus we must seek an explanation different from the intellectual view that casts everything in terms of a finality–in spite of what the Darwinians may say.

In his book 'L'Évolution du monde vivant' *[The Evolution of the Living World]* [1], M. Vernet cites a letter that Darwin wrote to Thomas Thorton Esq. in 1861. Darwin states quite clearly that he is aware of having failed to explain evolution :

«*But I believe in natural selection, not because, I can prove, in any single case, that it has changed one species into another, but because it groups and explains well (as it seems to me) a host of facts in classification, embryology, morphology, rudimentary organs, geological succession and distribution...*»

Darwin was perfectly well aware, therefore, that the theories he advanced concerned the possible influence of natural selection on *a species that did not, however, transform itself into another species.* Furthermore, when Darwin put forward the idea of natural selection as a tentative explanation of his objective observations, he was simply proposing a theory. By definition, a theory is no more than a hypothesis that for a while serves to link facts of various kinds by way of an explanation. While it may prove useful at a certain stage in human knowledge, however, it is the future that determines whether a certain hypothesis is valid or not. The validity of Darwin's theory has not yet been proven.

Unfortunately for Darwinism, the theory was used for ideological purposes. We are now much more familiar with the process of evolution, owing to more consistent data such as the information provided by paleontology and the natural sciences, as well as new knowledge, acquired since Darwin, concerning heredity (genetics)

1. Published by Plon, Paris, 1950. The fac-similé of Darwin's letter is contained in this book. M. Vernet notes that the letter is preserved at the British Museum (Ref. A DD MS. 37725f.6).

and biology (especially molecular biology.) In spite of this, we are still saddled with the theory formulated by Darwin over a century ago; there are those who do not wish to see its ideological success diminished. That is why we today have the 'neo-Darwinians' who hope to use modern discoveries to combine the basic idea of selection with new data. We shall see later on that a combination of this kind is also open to severe criticism.

I should like to conclude this discussion of Darwinism proper by turning once again to the opinions of P.-P. Grassé. The reason I have quoted this eminent specialist in evolution so often is that I consider his opinions to be extremely well-argued and logical. This is what P.-P. Grassé has to say about the influence of Darwin's work as a whole :

"It is significant–but often forgotten–that Darwin named the book that brought him fame, *On the Origin of Species*. He sought the mechanism through which one species transformed itself into another; he did not envisage the origin of the basic types of organization. He not only refused to give attention to the general problems concerning the unity of the organizational plan, but he actively distrusted them. He expresses this as follows : "It is so easy to hide our ignorance under such expressions as the 'plan of creation', 'unity of design', & c., and to think that we give an explanation when we only restate a fact." The expression 'plan of creation' does indeed suggest a tendentious interpretation which we reject. That does not mean, however, that Darwin's reasoning was correct when he refused to consider the predominant problems of evolution. In his eyes, natural selection explained everything; he therefore considered an

Two iguanas to Darwin :
Please listen to us! Contrary to your theory,
each of us has belonged to the same species
for millions and millions of years.

(This stamp was issued by the British Royal Mail in 1982
to commemorate the centenary of Darwin's death.)

animal in terms of a species. His whole system of explanation was conceived in such a way that he referred only to variations that did not go beyond the species. It is a strange fact, however, that Darwin never took the trouble to define what he meant by 'species', not even in the glossary that appears at the end of *On the Origin of Species.* "[1]

Neo-Darwinism

In order to realize the extent to which Darwin is still revered today, one has to have come into contact with the academic world in America, especially in the fields of biology, genetics or evolution. Darwin is venerated, however, in spite of the fact that his theory is outdated and his concepts extremely fragile. The criticism that may legitimately be levelled at Darwinism, as a result of the proven data on evolution collected by paleontologists, zoologists and botanists, exercises a certain influence on the opinions of specialists in Europe. It has virtually no impact on researchers in the United States, who uphold theories that are for the most part conceived in the laboratory. One is tempted to ask whether it is possible to be anything but a Darwinian in America. In some people's opinion, the idea of criticizing Darwin is the same as saying that the theories of Einstein are totally worthless. The difference between them lies in the fact that Einstein's theories were solidly based and their validity was subsequently demonstrated. There are indeed people in Europe who persist in their infatuation with the role of natural selection in evolution, but perhaps fewer than in the United States.

The predominant idea at the moment seems to be the integration into the system of newly acquired genetic discoveries : Natural selection no longer intervenes to favour the survival of the fittest, but rather in terms of probabilities. It operates through a statistical process that raises the likelihood that the fittest will be the individuals who transmit their characteristics. Thus the process of natural selection acts as the agent ensuring the preferential transmission of attributes registered in the genes. The idea of sexual selection lives again in the minds of the neo-Darwinians...

Genetics deals with the subject of heredity, and as we shall see

1. P.-P. Grassé, 'Biologie moléculaire, mutagénèse et évolution' *(Molecular Biology, Mutagenesis and Evolution)*, Masson, Paris, 1978.

very clearly later on, today's discoveries in this field allow us to arrive at certain very important theories and practical conclusions– for genetics deals with present-day phenomena. With regard to evolution, genetics is currently attempting to study mutations that modify certain minor characteristics, concentrating its research on living beings that reproduce very rapidly. As it happens, however, evolution that takes place in the animal kingdom over the course of time has a much greater effect than the minimal variations observed in present-day organisms. That is why zoologists specialising in evolution question the extrapolations of the geneticists; the latter choose the wrong method of applied study when investigating present-day organisms, and this leads them to mistaken interpretations of past events. In short, they are not studying the real questions of evolution.

If evolution had indeed occurred in the manner suggested by the Darwinians and neo-Darwinians–in other words as a result of minimal variations (which as far as we know leave living beings within the framework of their species)–how much time would have been required for the formation of the organized types that exist today? Tens of billions of years? Hundreds of billions? In actual fact, the amount of time needed for the transition from unicellular life forms to the most recent higher mammals was just over one billion years. Furthermore, examination of the transitions undergone by man from the Australopithecus to present-day Homo Sapiens indicate that modifications took place at amazing speed within a very small population (we know this from the rarity of fossils.) This is to be compared with the fact that for hundreds of millions of years bacteria and insects–such as cockroaches–have remained more or less identical in spite of the tremendous variety of individuals and genetic mutations. Neo-Darwinism takes no account of these fundamental points, thus invalidating the very basis of its theory.

We need an explanation of the variable speed of evolution that is different from the spontaneous, unpredictable mutations presented by the neo-Darwinians as the motivating force behind an evolution that is controlled by a so-called process of natural selection. This leads us to think that modern followers of Darwinian theory have no coherent explanation of evolution to offer us. Their explanatory suggestions–however brilliant–do not seem applicable to a real situation that requires real answers.

Sociobiology

With E.O. Wilson [1] and American sociobiology, which gave allegiance to neo-Darwinism, the explanatory theories of all human action, based on the strict correlation between human and animal motivations, have reached the height of their art. Indeed, E.O. Wilson has given a more detailed view of his opinions in a work published quite recently [2]. Wilson and his followers have studied the behaviour of animal communities, some of which –such as the termites– are remarkably well organized, and the conduct of man, whose actions Wilson considers to be entirely the result of impulses emanating from the genes. This leads to an 'animalization' of man that is scientifically unacceptable. If the damage caused by Wilson's ideas only affected the strict framework of theoretical interpretation, it would not be that serious. What is highly disturbing is that in the suggestions put forward for the practical application of this theory, man is relegated to the level of an insect, faithfully executing orders within an extremely well-organized animalistic society.

Wilson and the advocates of sociobiology further suggest that the scientist ought to exercise the right to modify man at will by genetic procedures. As we shall see later on, this would transform human society –supposedly for the better, in the eyes of those who uphold these theories– according so-called scientific bases. What this in fact amounts to is nothing other than the social ideal that was once constructed on principles of race. We all know that it led to the most widespread slaughter in the history of modern times and to the final collapse of the 'master race'. E.O. Wilson and sociobiology open prospects that are utterly degrading for mankind. I shall return to them in my discussion of what I call 'genetic manipulation' and others euphemistically call 'genetic engineering'.

1. E.O. Wilson, *Sociobiology. The New Synthesis*. Belknap Press of Harvard University Press. Cambridge (Mass) and London, 1975.
2. E.O. Wilson, *On Human Nature*. Harvard University Press. Cambridge (Mass), 1978.

ESSENTIAL FEATURES OF EVOLUTION
THAT SHOULD NOT BE OVERLOOKED

The preceding chapter drew attention to the gap separating two groups : On one hand the zoologists, whose study of evolution takes serious account of the discoveries of paleontology, thus enabling zoologists to establish the chronological succession of developments (with a few gaps, needless to say.) On the other hand, there are those who think they can reconstruct the course of evolution by using data observed in today's living beings, as well as laboratory researchers working on organisms that reproduce themselves rapidly, and studying the descendants of these organisms. Thus this group arrives at suggestions as to what may have taken place long ago.

No serious study of evolution can be undertaken without recourse to both groups. The first establishes the facts, and the second (especially the laboratory researchers) provides extremely helpful data to explain how events take place or may have taken place, and on a more general level, suggesting answers if there are any to be found.

What do each of these groups have to offer? The first lays before us concrete data on events that happened long ago, sometimes with a slight tendency to underplay the gaps in our knowledge of the order in which these events took place. By and large, however, the information provided deals with concrete facts. The second group seems either to have forgotten or not to have taken account of these events. Instead, it supplies us with explanatory theories which can hardly be said to apply to real facts or events. If we lose sight of reality, however, the most sophisticated reasoning can only lead to inaccurate statements : That is exactly what is currently happening in the case of certain theories, such as neo-Darwinism and others, as we shall see later on.

Let us therefore turn to the data supplied by those accustomed to objectively setting forth the facts of a history—for it is indeed a history—without deciding in advance the factors that may have influenced the course of evolution.

From the most elementary books on the natural sciences onward, we have been taught that the animal and vegetal species in existence today could be grouped according to certain characteristics. We also learned that there were many sorts of groups—in the broadest sense of the word—composed of families that all share a certain number of features. The number of groups has continued to increase with the passage of time, owing to knowledge newly acquired by zoology and also as a result of the discovery of fossilized animals that no longer exist today, having left us nothing but vestiges. All these data seem to increase the diversity of living beings.

The groupings established by naturalists and paleontologists have enabled us to distinguish compartments into which we can divide living beings who share a number of common characteristics. From this arise extremely important concepts. For example, the existence of an order in which the various categories appeared throughout the different eras, and the fact that each category tended to transform itself in a very specific way as time passed.

From the most ancient times onward, organisms began to appear (as stated earlier) that acquired a more and more complex structure—without, however, creating any kind of disorder or anarchy. After a period of one or two billion years, distinguished by the existence of living beings containing simple structures (although already extremely complex from a biological point of view), organizational types developed that included today's members of the animal kingdom, as well as extinct species. The phyla in question did not, however, continue developing indefinitely to the detriment of more simple forms. A halt was reached roughly 350 million years ago, the period in which the first vertebrates appeared. Since then, particular classes of living beings have formed within a phylum which preserve the main features of the phylum while acquiring new characteristics. For example, in the case of the vertebrates, the birth of cyclostomes (fish without jaws, such as lampreys) was accompanied by the appearance of fish that, in certain instances, led to the formation of the amphibians (batrachians, such as the frog); among the latter, some amphibians gave birth to the reptiles, from which one group detached itself to form the mammals, while another later became the birds. Of all the living beings thus formed, the birds came last, appearing some 135 million years ago. Since the birds, no new class has appeared in the animal kingdom.

A remarkable phenomenon is the fact that the characteristics of a class gradually increase over successive generations, while now and again, secondary branches appear which acquire new specific features that constitute the origin of new forms. Some of the branches proliferate and survive while others disappear more or less quickly, but these secondary branches never represent the beginnings of new phyla. There was a period in which the general organizational plans appeared, and once that period was over and the plans fulfilled, there were no subsequent plans. Henceforth, all that could appear would be subdivisions.

The events of evolution took place at highly variable speeds right up until the time the final form was attained that marked a halt in the process. As a result, there are species among today's living organisms that quickly acquired their definitive form and have retained it until the present day : for example certain molluscs, insects, and fishes that have remained the same, while closely related forms have undergone a long and far-reaching process of evolution. Thus the coelacanth has not evolved for 200 or 300 million years. Vestiges of primitive phyla are very common in nature, indicating forms that have remained at an initial stage without evolving at all : for example bacteria, unicellular organisms, sponges, jellyfishes, various coral, and particularly prolific insects, of which there exist roughly 100,000 species for a single order (the collembolae, for instance.) As opposed to this, there are examples of revivals after a long halt : Zoologists point to families that experienced an intense period of evolution, only to peter out later on. While there is quite clearly a lack of continuity in evolution as a whole, this does not exclude the *ever-present order* in the general march of events.

Within the complexity of organization, there nevertheless appears a progressive tendency toward a type that is finally to be constituted, containing of course variations both small and great. The horse is always cited as an example of a type whose evolution took place on several continents, gradually arriving at its definitive form in spite of the diversity of environments.

The irreversible evolution that occurs within an order creates new forms by increasing the complexity of structures with the passage of time. When all is said and done, there is a direct link between the passing of time and the complexity of organization.

One of the best and most readily understood examples of this growing complexity is the evolution of the nervous system in the animal kingdom. Originally non-existent, a 'rough outline' appeared in the form of cells that contained the ability to feel; this was followed by the beginnings of a system of sensory and motor relations leading to the tremendous complexity now present in the higher vertebrates. With the development of the brain, an extraordinary ability to retain information was acquired, allowing innate features to manifest themselves, and, in the case of man, permitting the psyche to develop at the same time as acquired behaviour, while man's innate behaviour correspondingly decreased. We shall return to these fundamental concepts in Part Two of the present work, which deals with man.

This notion of the production of new and ever-more complex structures completely rules out the effects of chance. Unpredictable, fortuitous variations—even when corrected by natural selection—could never have ensured such progression in perfect order. The progression implies that the variations were *simultaneous and coordinated* so as to obtain a growing organizational complexity. Science is able to analyse the phenomenon; it knows that the existence of genes implies that a particular phylum cannot produce a certain class derived from another phylum, and that a particular family from a specific class cannot one day appear in another class. Evolution is quite obviously oriented, even though the term may shock those who will only acknowledge phenomena whose existence can be explained—as if man could explain everything. Since science is unable to solve the enigma, however, some people cast it aside and refuse to incorporate it into their way of thinking. Thus the essential features of evolution in the animal kingdom are not taken into consideration by those who are unwilling to finish a study by admitting that they are at a loss to account for the reasons behind the phenomenon. A theory such as 'chance and necessity' will provide a clear illustration of this attitude, as we shall see.

THE ROLE OF CHANCE AND NECESSITY

Since the structure of living beings seems to have progressed in a perfectly coordinated way over the course of time, how is it that in this context people have paradoxically come to speak of chance? Is there really any need to stop and examine the theory that chance plays an active part? Certainly not, if we take account of the known facts of evolution. We must indeed examine the role of chance, however, in view of the fact that it has been fiercely defended by some and has attracted so much attention that the inaccuracy of the theory needs to be pointed out.

As for necessity, which should here be understood to mean 'the impossibility of the contrary', it is difficult to find any foundation for such an idea. In the explanation of the phenomena discussed here, the place occupied by necessity is, to say the least, extremely dubious.

We have already discussed the role of chance in the origins and evolution of life. The philosophers of Antiquity, ignorant as they were of the realities of the universe, may be excused for conceiving (like Democritus) that eternal matter acted to produce all the cosmic systems and everything in the universe, animate and inanimate forms alike. While Democritus could not have had the faintest idea of cell structure, however, the same cannot be said of today's scientists, especially when they are experts in molecular biology. What is one to think, therefore, when the role of chance is upheld by people who are aware of the immense complexity of living matter as a result of their own brilliant discoveries and analyses of it? Basic common sense tells us that the very last factor capable of explaining the existence of a highly complex organization is chance.

Even if we move our attention from the cell itself to its tiniest molecular elements, we shall see that physicists and chemists have long ago abandoned the theory that the cell was formed by chance :

Indeed, in order for the smallest macromolecules of a cell to form as a result of repeated attempts, such enormous quantities of matter would have to have been processed that they would have filled literally colossal masses—on a scale comparable to the volume of the earth itself. This is totally inconceivable.

Oparine, a modern Russian biologist who is a well-known materialist, rejects outright the theory of chance in the formation of life : "The entire network of metabolic reactions is not only strictly coordinated, but also oriented toward the perpetual preservation and reproduction of the totality of conditions set by the external environment. This highly organized orientation characteristic of life cannot be the result of chance." (From an article entitled 'État actuel du problème de l'origine de la vie et ses perspectives' *[The Current State of the Problem of the Origin of Life and Its Future Perspectives]*, which appeared in the French journal 'Biogenèse' *[Biogenesis]*, Paris, 1967, p. 19.)

In his work, *The Origin of Life*, Oparine draws particularly relevant comparisons to help the layman see the illogicality of theories pointing toward chance. As he wrote in 1954 :

"It is as if one jumbled together the printing blocks representing the twenty-eight letters of the alphabet, in the hope that by chance they will fall into the pattern of a poem that we know. Only through knowledge and careful arrangement of the letters and words in a poem, however, can we produce the poem from the letters."

There are of course certain theories that can be put forward, but some of them are quite obviously absurd. Oparine cites the following example in his book : "Physicists state that it is theoretically possible for the table at which I am writing to rise by chance, due to the orientation in the same direction of the thermic movement of all its molecules. Nobody is likely, however, to take account of this in his experimental work or in his practical activity as a whole."

I owe these important quotations from Oparine to the highly documented book by Claude Tresmontant entitled 'Comment se pose aujourd'hui le problème de l'existence de Dieu' *[How Does the Problem of the Existence of God Appear Today?]* [1]; they appear in Claude Tresmontant's commentary on the theories of J. Monod published in 'Le Hasard et la Nécessité' *[Chance and Necessity]* [2].

As early as 1967, J. Monod had stated in his inaugural speech at the Collège de France that 'any and every fortuitous accident...' in

1. Published by Seuil, Paris, 1971.
2. Published by Seuil, Paris, 1970.

the reproduction of the genetic programme throughout evolution explained the creation of new structures : "Evolution, the emergence of complex structures from simple forms, is therefore the result of the very imperfections in the system preserving the structures represented by the cell... It may be said that the *same fortuitous events* which, in an inanimate system, would accumulate to the point where all structures disappeared, lead, in the biosphere, to the creation of new and increasingly complex structures." Claude Tresmontant quotes another passage from J. Monod which appeared in a French journal entitled 'Raison présente' *[Present Reason]*, n° 5, 1968 : "The only possible source of evolution has been in the fortuitous accidents that have occured in the structure of D.N.A. They are what are known as 'mutations'."

It is difficult to understand why J. Monod therefore decided that *chance alone* was the intervening factor in this case. After all, he himself stressed his ignorance–an ignorance we all share–concerning the origins of genetic information: "The major problem is the origin of the genetic code and the mechanism by which it is expressed. Indeed, one cannot talk so much of a 'problem' as of a genuine enigma." In fact, however, the enigma is twofold : It not only affects the origin of the genetic code, but also the increase in the data contained in the genes leading to the birth of more and more complex structures; an increase which, as we shall see later on, is expressed through chemical compounds.

The theory of chance as the force creating highly organized structures is at odds with the facts. We have already seen that evolution, in all its shapes and forms, takes place in an ordered fashion, complete with genuine lineages observing an orientation that is perfectly clear. We cannot logically argue therefore, that 'fortuitous accidents'–to use J. Monod's phrase–could have produced anything but chaos. We know in fact that within the same overall plan, concordant variations must combine over periods of time which are often very long, in order for entirely new forms to appear. It is hardly surprising, therefore, that eminent zoologists such as P.-P. Grassé, who are thoroughly familiar with the question, are incensed by explanations which take no account of the real situation. Among P.-P. Grassé's many critical comments, I shall quote the following observation concerning an aspect of the evolution of the mammals from the reptiles, an event that lasted some 50 million years : "In the mammal, all the sensory organs evolved at more or less the same time. When we try to imagine just what their formation required in terms of simultaneous, or almost simultaneous muta-tions, all of them taking place at the right moment and capable of fulfilling the needs expected of them, we remain speechless at the sight of so much harmony, so many fortunate coincidences, all of them due to the unique and triumphant role of chance." ('L'Evolution du vivant' *[The Evolution of Living Organisms]*.)

In view of the fact that J. Monod received the Nobel Prize for Medicine, it behoves us to ask the following question : How is it possible for such an eminent scientist to put forward a theory such as this? The answer is quickly found : It lies in a doctrinal system that rests on a postulate that its author calls "the postulate of the objectivity of nature... the systematic refusal to admit that any interpretation of phenomena cast in terms of a 'final cause'–meaning plan–can lead to a 'true' knowledge... While the organism observes the physical laws, it also surpasses them, thus devoting itself entirely to the pursuit and realization of its own plan..." This means that henceforth only those factors that add new possibilities to the organism will be acceptable... We must also show our admiration for the "miraculous efficiency in the performances of living beings, ranging from bacteria to man..." The ideological ulterior motive is patently obvious : It consists in the refusal to accept the existence of any organization in nature, and it leaves room only for individual 'performances.'

In referring to the accidental alterations in the genes of living organisms and their influence on the evolution of living beings, J. Monod employs terms that do not even allow us to think that his personal view might one day be subject to revision : "We say that these alterations are accidental, that they take place by chance. Since they constitute the *only* source of possible modifications in the genetic code, which is itself the *only* repository of the organism's hereditary structures, it must *necessarily* follow that chance, and *only* chance is the source of any new development or creation in the biosphere. Pure chance, and *only* chance–freedom, blind but absolute–the very root of the edifice we call evolution : This central concept of modern biology is no longer a mere hypothesis among other possible or conceivable hypotheses. It is the *only* conceivable hypothesis, the *only* one compatible with facts acquired through observation and experimentation. There is no reason to suppose (or to hope) that our concepts on this point should or even can be revised."

In fact, however, the concept of 'pure chance', 'chance and only chance', 'freedom, blind but absolute–the very root of... evolution' has received some hard knocks from P.-P. Grassé. In 'L'Evolution du vivant' *[The Evolution of Living Organisms]*, the eminent naturalist indicates that the problem of the transfer of information within the cell could be much more complex that J. Monod had foreseen when he stated that it was inconceivable henceforth to approach the problem from any angle other his (i.e. Monod's) own point of view.

Let us first stress the fact that in the genes, as we shall see further on, D.N.A. (desoxyribonucleic acid) is the basic chemical material or vehicle for biological information. The information is transferred to the cellular cytoplasm by a different substance, R.N.A. (ribonucleic acid). In Monod's theory, the transfer of information is always referred to in terms of a flow from the D.N.A. toward the R.N.A., and never in the reverse direction. In actual fact, however, the unexpected and the unforeseen can indeed occur.

The following is the objection presented in 'L'Evolution du vivant' *[The Evolution of Living Organisms]* :

"The dogma of the immutability of D.N.A., which is always presented as the unique keeper and distributor of biological information destined to flow in one direction only, has been put forward by eminent biochemists (Watson, Crick, etc.) and geneticists (Jacob, Monod, etc.) Three years ago, in 1970, J. Monod made the following statement on the subject in 'Le Hasard et la Nécessité' *[Chance and Necessity]*, pp. 124-125 : "It has never been observed, nor is it even conceivable, that information is ever transferred in the reverse direction..."

P.-P. Grassé's objection continues in the following terms :

"The ink of these lines was hardly dry when the denial came, sharp and incontrovertible. The logic of living things—which, by the way, was the logic of the said biologist and not of nature—was totally overturned and the fine edifice deeply flawed.

"The discovery of enzymes able to use viral R.N.A. as a matrix for the synthesis of D.N.A. is regarded as a revolution in molecular biology.

"It is also considered", writes P.-P. Grassé in a footnote, "to be the most important discovery concerning the role of viruses in the formation of cancers. Several R.N.A. viruses create D.N.A. replicas that are carcinogenic."

Further on, P.-P. Grassé outlines the new contributions made by studies conducted before (1964), during (1970) and after (1971 and 1972) the publication of J. Monod's work. P.-P. Grassé then draws the following conclusion :

"The studies outlined above show that a mechanism exists which, in certain circumstances, supplies information that comes from outside the organism and integrates it into the D.N.A. of the genetic code. For an evolutionist, this fact is of immense importance."

The dogma of necessity put forward by J. Monod is a long way from explaining why the organisms the zoologists call 'stock forms', which are the great-ancestors of today's types, have survived down to the present day and even live side by side with the modern forms descended from them. The same may be said of the unicellular organisms that still survive today, or even of older members of the living world, such as bacteria : How can their survival be explained?

In order to support his theory of the 'miraculous efficiency in the performances of living beings', J. Monod records in his book the following story (which is not based on any paleolontological data whatsoever) :

"The reason the tetrapod vertebrates appeared and were able to develop into the extraordinary range of animals that we know as the amphibians, the reptiles, the birds and the mammals, is that a primitive fish originally 'chose' to explore the dry land. There, however, it was only able to move about by leaping awkwardly. ('Le Hasard et la Nécessité' *[Chance and Necessity]*, pp. 142-143."

P.-P. Grassé concludes with the following remarks on the above statement :

"What makes us particularly unwilling to accept the story of the little fish–the 'Magellan of evolution'–is the fact that the boleophthalmidae and periophthalmidae (mud skippers) perform this very 'experiment'. They scuttle across the mud, climb the roots of mangrove trees, and raise themselves on their pectoral fins, just as if the fins were short limbs. They have lived in this way for millions of years, and although they never stop leaping about–awkwardly or not–their fins insist on remaining as they are, rather than transforming themselves into limbs. These animals really are not very understanding."

THE COMPLEXITY OF CELLULAR
ORGANIZATION AND THE GENES

Now that we have reviewed the explanatory theories of Antiquity and have shown that more recent theories–such as Darwinism, or the concept of chance and necessity–are unacceptable, it is time to try and find our way through highly complex scientific discoveries toward a clearer view of the problem. In several instances, we have indeed already touched on some of these discoveries in order to ensure a better understanding of the subject at hand, but if we are to arrive at a more accurate idea of the causes that engendered the sequence of events whose broad outlines we know already, we must enter into detail. This means knowing more about the organization of the cell, and in particular the role of the genes contained in the chromosomes. It was indeed the events that took place within the cell that determined the progression of changes that as a whole constitued evolution.

The following account of facts concerning the cell may perhaps seem a little complex to some, while to others, who already know something of the subject, it may seem over-simplified and in need of more detailed information. I would ask the former to try and grasp the data described, for they will be of help in understanding what is to follow, and I entreat the latter to refer to the publications I shall cite, in which they will find facts that complement my own.

Specialists in molecular biology, genetics and the study of chromosomes have provided information on cellular functions and heredity that is extremely useful in interpreting phenomena connected with evolution. The present work is not intended to provide an exhaustive study of the question; those wishing to consult a bibliography on these subjects are advised to turn to the three excellent articles in the *Encyclopaedia Universalis* contributed respectively by P. Kourilsky, P. L'Héritier, and, for the study of chromosomes, M. Picard and J. de Grouchy. I shall moreover be using many of their data and ideas in the following section.

Essential Data Concerning the Biochemical Organization of the Cell

Chemical changes are constantly taking place within each and every cell. The living matter contained in the cell is constantly renewed, and the cells renew themselves by division within the organs, some of which–such as the blood–possess a very marked capacity for self-renewal. In this context, the reproductive cells should also be mentioned, which ensure the perpetuation of the species.

In order for all these functions to continue, constant exchanges of matter and energy with the surrounding environment must take place, resulting in the production of macromolecules in the cell from simpler chemical elements. For this to happen, not only the two components that are to combine must be present, there must also be what are called 'catalysts', agents that have the property of acting in infinitely small quantities to trigger the chemical reaction but which remain unchanged once the reaction has taken place. Each catalyst is specific to the reaction required. The production of protein in living matter, which results from the synthesis of simpler components, calls for the intervention of catalysts which in this case are enzymes, each enzyme containing the unique property of provoking the synthesis of a particular protein.

In their turn, the enzymes must be produced, and every cell possesses a system for this purpose. The basic element of this system is a proteinic macromolecule of tremendous complexity, called desoxyribonucleic acid (D.N.A.) The other chemical components 'hook onto' this basic substance, and with varying degrees of complexity ensure the production of the enzymes that are to provoke the proteinic syntheses required for life to exist.

In the simplest living organisms, D.N.A. is in direct contact with the substance of the cell, the cytoplasm : An example of this are the bacteria which do not contain a nucleus. In other, more organized animal and vegetal cells, however, the D.N.A. is located inside the nucleus of the cell within the chromosomes. This means that it only intervenes indirectly in the process of synthesizing living matter : It simply acts as the keeper of all the data (which taken together constitute a parcel of information) required by the reactions, using the intermediary of 'messengers' that take copies from it (the

D.N.A.) and carry them to other parts of the cytoplasm, such as the ribosomes. The 'messages' are transmitted via ribonucleic acid, or R.N.A.

The message transferred from the nucleus to the cellular cytoplasm via R.N.A. does not arrive directly however. The messenger R.N.A. in fact operates with the help of a second R.N.A., a transfer R.N.A., which is effective in transmitting the message, after which the messenger R.N.A. is destroyed. This detail indicates the complexity of the communications system, which is in fact far more complicated than it appears in this simplified outline, for the message is actually transmitted in code...

Thus we begin to gain an idea of the countless interrelations that exist within the cell, complete with its central command 'headquarters', its messengers, and its intermediary organs which play a part in the renewal of living matter. Another important point is that the central command adresses its orders to specific messengers in order to trigger the vast number of chemical syntheses that condition an infinite variety of tasks to be performed. We are therefore in the presence of an organized system that is of considerable functional size, even though its volume is very tiny indeed. It is a system that conditions all the activities of the cell, including its reproduction, which is how it comes to play its part in heredity and thereby in evolution.

Every cell contains D.N.A. chains : In the case of bacteria, whose dimensions are measured in $1/1,000$ of a millimetre, D.N.A. forms a tape whose length is measured in millimetres. The tape is therefore quite short in this instance, although in the case of Escherichia Coli, it has been calculated to be roughly 5,000 times longer than the maximun dimension of the bacteria in question. A length of one millimetre is quite considerable in molecular terms, and on one millimetre of D.N.A. tape are placed an infinite number of complex chemical components, each of which conditions every single function of the bacteria. In the case of man, for one single cell, the D.N.A. tape is long enough to be counted in metres. As for the total length of D.N.A. tape contained in a human being, it is greater than the distance separating the earth from the sun (P. Kourilsky.)

The D.N.A. tapes, which measure over one metre in length for each cell, are the keepers of the hereditary characteristics transmitted to us by our parents. They convey all the information that each and every cell in our body can use. As the life of the embryo progresses, the cells become differentiated, acquiring special functions and constituting all our organs in accordance with commands issued by the genes. This entire system is miniaturized to an extreme degree; a D.N.A. tape that is over one metre long is infinitely thin, its thickness being measured in angströms (one ten-millionth of a millimetre.)

D.N.A. has a spiral structure in the shape of a double helix, one tape being twisted around the other. Specialists in molecular biology have compared it to a photograph accompanied by its negative. When a replica of the tape is produced during cellular division, the two chains separate and each chain serves as a mould for the production of a complementary chain; exactly as the negative of a photograph provides us with a positive print and vice versa. Thus we arrive at two copies that are identical to the original, providing nothing has gone wrong during processing.

The system's capacity for production and the diversity of the end result are quite considerable. A bacteria such as Escherichia Coli can synthesize as many as 3,000 different kinds of proteins. Over half of these have been identified. Human cells contain a thousand times more D.N.A. than Escherichia Coli. Thus we see the immense capacity of cells in higher organisms to produce extremely diversified living substances : The list of proteins that can be synthesized in this way is far from complete.

It is important to note the fantastic manner in which the D.N.A. tape grows longer and longer as it passes from the cells of primitive organisms to the higher organisms : At the bottom of the scale it is one millimetre long, but when it reaches man, it is over one metre long (P. Kourilsky.) Later on, we shall see that we may speak of an increase in the genes that corresponds to the growing complexity in the functions and structure of all living beings. The list of the genes is no more complete, however, than that of the cellular proteins. The implication inherent in these observations is that evolution must have been intimately linked with the acquisition of new genes, which was henceforth to be its *sine qua non*. The quantity of information recorded continued gradually to increase over the course of time.

The above information concerning the length of the tape on which the genes have been placed seems to be more meaningful than the weight of the D.N.A. contained in each cell. In P.-P. Grassé's book, 'L'Evolution du vivant' [*The Evolution of Living Organisms*], figures are provided relative to the weight of D.N.A. in the cells of living beings located at a more or less high level in the scale of structures. The weight of D.N.A. varies considerably from one species to another, but without any apparent connection with the degree of evolution. This does not seem to contradict what has been said above, however, for there is not just one D.N.A. but several

D.N.A.'s whose molecular weight fluctuates according to the source from which it was extracted (thymus, wheatgerm, bacteria, etc.), the proportion ranging from one to several hundred (M. Privat de Garilhe.) The chemical complexity depends on the number of elements held by the tape. For example, the D.N.A. of *Bacillus subtilis* has a molecular mass of at least 230 million, while the D.N.A. of herpetic virus has a mass on the order of 100 million, and the mass of the single-stranded D.N.A. of bacteriophage is some 1,600,000 (M. Privat de Garilhe.) For a simple body, such as water, which is composed of two atoms of hydrogen and one of oxygen, the molecular weight is 18, the figures representing the degree of chemical complexity : A fact that needs to be kept in mind.

The above comments concerning, D.N.A. contain reservations, for it is obviously not possible to use a regular balance to weigh D.N.A.(the scale of measurement is in this case counted in billionths of a milligram.) These estimations are based on our knowledge of the simplest D.N.A. (simplest from a chemical point of view), corrected by extrapolations derived from measuring the length of molecules with the aid of an electron microscope. The figures are subject to revision, and so are the conclusions we may draw from them. These observations are presented simply to give an idea of the complexity of the organization in question. They illustrate the notion that in order to grasp what evolution means, one must take account of ultra-microscopic studies of the cell and of data provided by molecular biology, both of which have considerably increased our knowledge. Sometimes, however, we encounter contradictions on points that some people consider to be of little importance, while others regard them as highly significant. There are certain currently accepted ideas that will be subject to revision in the future. The fact remains however, that science has accumulated a sufficient number of established facts for certain general concepts to emerge both clearly and logically from the data acquired by cellular biology.

The Chromosomes

In describing the extraordinary biochemical complex we call the cell, we have so far only briefly mentioned the role D.N.A. plays in retaining hereditary characteristics, among its many other functions. As we have seen, in the case of the most primitive unicellular beings, such as the bacteria, only one D.N.A. tape is present : There is no nucleus. In the case of cellular organisms containing a more elaborate structure however, the nucleus appears, in which the chromosomes are concentrated : It is in the chromosomes that we find the genes. Before proceeding, however, to an analysis of the role played by the genes (especially in evolution), we must refresh our memory of certain ideas concerning the chromosomes.

Their very name is a direct reference to one of their characteristics : The reason Waldeyer gave them this name in 1888 was that he had noticed how these differentiated elements within the nucleus could be stained with colourings the moment the cell began to divide. In organisms that possess a sexual reproductive system, the chromosomes are arranged in identical pairs. This distribution is extremely important because it maintains the number of chromosomes–always the same in the same species–during the reproductive process. When it arrives at maturity, each cell–whether spermatozoon or ovule–possesses only half of the chromosomes of the species. As soon as the two reproductive cells unite, the even number of chromosomes is re-established (46 in the case of man.)

One of the chromosomes has a role to play in determining sex; it belongs to the male. The following is an outline of how the process works : The female possesses a pair of chromosomes that are arbitrarily designated as XX; the male possesses another pair designated XY. Since the number of chromosomes is reduced (meiosis) during the formation of reproductive cells, the spermatozoa are divided into two groups. One group contains X and the other Y. If the X ovule is fertilized by a spermatozoon carrying an X, a female (XX) will be formed. If it is fertilized by a Y spermatozoon, the result will be a male (XY.)

The distribution of X and Y factors in the spermatozoa is almost exactly equal, which is why the number of girls and boys born is practically the same. Nevertheless, if the spermatozoa of the future father were successfully separated into two groups and the woman artificially inseminated with one of the groups, a couple would be able to decide whether they wanted a boy or a girl. This is not at all a utopian vision, for the 'manipulation' of human spermatozoa is now sufficiently advanced for a project such as this to become a reality : with the consequences that such a practice would entail, as may well be imagined. Fortunately however, human reproduction has so far continued without factors such as the above intervening in the distribution of sex–the balance has been maintained by nature.

Chromosomes are composed of D.N.A., R.N.A. and various proteins. The D.N.A. carries the genes; these are not subject to renewal, contrary to the other components of the cell. D.N.A. can only be renewed when the cells divide. The quantity of R.N.A. varies from one cell to another and from one moment to another. In performing its role as messenger carrying the information contained in the genes, R.N.A. is constantly being renewed in the chromosomes; it constitutes a witness to the activities of the genes and ceases to be produced when the genes have no message to transmit.

Irregularities in the chromosomes can produce extremely serious consequences; spontaneous abortion (30% of such cases are due to failures in the regular division of the chromosomes), and various illnesses that occur with differing degrees of frequency, the most well-known of which is Mongolism (trisomy 21, an illness that affects roughly one child in 700.) Modifications such as these either result in the death of the embryo or the birth of severely deformed individuals. Over and above this however, living organisms are able to change during the course of reproduction, even within the framework of a reproductive pattern that tends to conform to the model provided by the individual's forebears. The classic experiments carried out on vegetals by the Czech monk Gregor Mendel in the mid-nineteenth century (which did not become famous until after his death) provide theoretical support to the research undertaken at the beginning of the twentieth century : They led to the discovery of the genes and their localization in the chromosomes.

The Genes

Today, it is an established fact that the genes are segments of D.N.A. molecules. Through the action of the D.N.A., the process of which has already been outlined above, they command the renewal of the proteinic molecules that constitute the living matter of the cell. This biochemical activity modifies the properties of the molecules in the cell, thus influencing the way the cell functions as well as the production of specific structures which allow the cells to play clearly defined roles. From this point of view, one might say that the gene is the smallest part of the D.N.A. molecule capable of inducing a permanent characteristic.

While the basic idea is admitted that the more complex the structure of an animal, the more likely it is to possess a larger quantity of genes, specialists in genetics are not in agreement on the number of genes involved. When they lead to mutations, the genes are the object of close study. In the case of the drosophila, a fly which, from this point of view, particularly lends itself to laboratory study, the number of genes counted is quite large : anything from

5,000 to 15,000! How many genes does man contain? No-one really knows[1]. Besides, the relationship between the number of features and the quantity of genes is not at all clear. Some observers claim that a spectific enzyme corresponds to each gene, but a single enzyme may in fact give birth to several features.

The genes are responsible for may different functions. From this we may deduce that the primordial functions that characterize a phylum depend on certain genes which have been operating, as it were, since the very beginnings of the phylum in question. As evolution progressed, however, and one after another the class, order, family, genus and species appeared, the genes intervened successively and specifically for each major characteristic. The interventions occurred at more and more recent periods in time, and they were perfectly coordinated chronologically; it is to them that living beings owe their form.

Zoologists have many questions to ask on this subject. In 'L'Evolution du vivant' [*The Evolution of Living Organisms*], P.-P. Grassé raises some extremely important points, as follows :

– D.N.A. is just not present in the chromosomes; it is also active in the mitochondriae and other differentiated cellular elements. But what is the role of this extra-nuclear D.N.A.?

– The hormones play a part in triggering genetic activity. "A constant flow of information streams from the nuclear D.N.A., while another floods toward it, thus setting it into action. Mutual communications between the cytoplasm and the chromosomes, and vice versa, are a constant necessity" (P.-P. Grassé.) He goes on to cite experiments proving the influence of the cytoplasm on the chromosomes. As we have already seen above, in P.-P. Grassé's criticism of J. Monod's theory (according to which information could only flow toward the D.N.A.), the dogma of a one-way stream of information has today been completely disproven.

All of the observations quoted above lead us to suppose that environment has an influence ou the genes, which in their turn modify structures. P.-P. Grassé gives examples taken from the vegetable kingdom and concludes that : "The rule stating that a gene will always determine the same characteristic–unless it is the subject of a mutation–is too rigid." In all likelihood, "the gene emits the same information, but the substances replying to its messages

---

1. Estimates range from 100,000 to 1,000,000; lower figures have also been suggested (30,000?)

react in different ways according to circumstances." All these comments indicate the fantastic complexity of the system and the suggested importance of multiple interactions. We have come a long way from the 'freedom, blind but absolute' put forward in the theory that attempts to explain everything in terms of 'chance'.

THE GENES: THEIR ROLE IN EVOLUTION AND OTHER PROCESSES

The Role of the Genes in Evolution. Mutations.

In the light of the data described above, how can we approach the role of the genes in evolution? Simply expressed, there are two radically different ways of tackling the problem: The first is employed by the geneticists. It is based on the observation of *present-day* facts; for example, calculations of genetic variations in populations that exist today, from which are drawn explanatory theories. The second method is used by zoologists and paleontologists. It involves the examination of material from the *past*, data to which the first group do not attach the same importance. In the survey that is to follow, we shall see that the opposition of the two methods has repercussions on the concepts of evolution entertained by the two groups.

In view of what we have already said about the infinite complexity of the chemical structure of the genes, and in view of the manner in which copies are produced during cellular division, it is perfectly possible to suppose that the slightest modification in the structure of the D.N.A. molecule may affect the cell concerned and all those engendered by it. This is indeed the case when the modification affects the male and female cells responsible for reproduction (germinal cells): It causes an alteration in the genetic code. In such conditions, a new characteristic appears in the individual which is passed on to its descendants: This constitutes a mutation, and the phenomenon is known as mutagenesis. It affects animals and vegetals alike, the most primitive life forms as well as those with a more complex organization (i.e. those containing a nucleus.) In the case of primitive forms, the mutation affects the D.N.A. present in the cytoplasm (bacteria are an example of this), in the case of more complex forms, it influences the genes held by the D.N.A. in the nucleus. The reason the mutation is considered to be fortuitous is that it is totally unpredictable, both in terms of the moment it will strike and also the place in which it will affect the D.N.A. molecule.

The impact the mutation has on the individual may be so great that the form concerned cannot survive the mutagenesis (in which case the mutation is said to affect lethal genes); on the other hand, the phenomenon may induce minor modifications which may prove to be recessive over the following generations.

In this way, on the D.N.A. tape of human cells, which is over one metre long, tiny genetic alterations are present which provide the individual with the characteristics that make him different from other people. It is these alterations that cause him more or less to resemble his parents or grandparents, and which even pass down the generations distinctive family features, such as the nose typical of the Bourbon kings of France. Sometimes, very serious phenomena can occur, such as illnesses connected with sex which affect the female X chromosome : A case in point is hemophilia, which mainly affects males, even though it is transmitted by females who remain immune to the disease. The male descendants of Queen Victoria of England suffered from this illness. Apart from these basically pathological mutations, most minor mutations tend to be recessive.

In view of the above, the question of evolution might at first glance seem fairly simple : The phenomenon of mutagenesis could be seen to account for all the hereditary variations which have accumulated over successive generations, thereby causing the evolution of living beings. There are a number of geneticists who subscribe to this theory. What is difficult to accept, however, is that in order for this theory to be valid, the mutations would have had to occur in a *chronologically perfect order* at *exactly the right moment* in time to arrive at the addition or subtraction of organs, or to effect a change of some kind in certain functions. It is perfectly clear, however, that these mutations essentially occur in a *disorderly fashion*. At this point, the geneticists who put forward hypotheses founded on calculations concerning present-day populations and who claim to have found an answer in this, part company from those who study the events of the past. The latter have perfect confidence in the findings of the former, as regards the properties of the genes, but they claim to see many shortcomings in theories that account for the inscription on the D.N.A. tape of new data that will become hereditary in the course of time. The second group does indeed seem to be infinitely more exacting than the first about the demonstrative value of certain–perfectly proven–facts concerning the genes.

First of all, however, the geneticists would have to arrive at a figure for the possible number of spontaneous mutations : So far, this figure has not been found. For one gene over an interval separating two generations, the estimated number is 1/10,000 (P. L'Héritier.) There are also a number of mutations that are neutral from the point of view of evolution. They form the source of individual characteristics, but they do not go beyond the framework of the species, and the individual thus retains all the attributes of that species. "We are a long way from the billions of billions of 'usable' variations mentioned by certain geneticists. The so-called usable variations are far fewer in number, a fact which renders even more problematic the idea of a 'good' mutation occurring at the right moment" (P.-P. Grassé.) We should not confuse the process of fortuitous mutation, which is responsible for the personal characteristics of the individual, with the active part played by mutations as the prime force behind the process of evolution.

The idea of evolution signifies progressive transformations on a very large scale. For example, the evolution of insects affected their entire organism in very strict order. The transformation of organs took place slowly but steadily over successive stages—for example, it took the mammals 80 million years to lose their reptilian features—and in an order that is incompatible with the arrival of random mutations.

In addition to the facts noted above, which result from paleontological investigation, genetic research provides us with data based on the most primitive organisms living today. These are the bacteria, an easy subject of study because they reproduce within the space of twenty minutes. It is thus possible to follow the progress of thousands of generations, among which mutations are found in the D.N.A. molecule. But what is the practical result of these mutations? Small-scale variations : The species remains the same, as it has done for hundreds of millions of years! As for the transition from the bacteria or the blue algae to organisms containing a cellular structure with a nucleus, an event that may well have occured one billion years ago, it is reasonable to suppose that environmental conditions were very different from those of today. Because of this, it is difficult to imagine that the mutations observed in today's bacteria are exactly the same as those produced in past ages.

The same mystery surrounds plants and animals that have not evolved at all in millions of years, even though they may have undergone fortuitous mutations. In this context, zoologists cite the case of the common cockroach, which, as far as they can tell, has hardly evolved at all since the primary era. The same applies to the 'panchronic' species, thus named because they have survived through the ages without any change, such as the opposum, certain limuli (marine insects with gills, commonly called king crabs) and various vegetals, none of which have been affected by mutations.

Objections have been raised on the above point, for certain observers maintain that panchronic species survive unchanged because they live in confined environments where conditions are not subject to much variation (for example, animals living in caves or in the depths of the sea.) While this may hold true for certain species living in such environments, it is not easily accepted by anyone who has travelled and has seen cockroaches present in many different parts of the world.

Other Points Which Need to Be Explained

It is very difficult to say whether the location of the genes on the helix-shaped D.N.A. tapes at the level of the chromosomes has any effect on the properties of the genes. Experiments have enabled scientists to separate and reunite fragments, even from one chromosome to another, but they have given positive and negative results that do not lead to any conclusions. As far as our own origins are concerned, the normal position of certain genes on human chromosomes is no more conclusive than the above.

It is possible for the number of chromosomes within a single species to vary. We find this in certain small nocturnal rodents (jerboae) which, in Senegal, have varying numbers of chromosomes : One group counts thirty-seven for the males and thirty-six for the females; another group possesses twenty-three for the males and twenty-two for the females. Nevertheless, the two groups are identical, displaying the same genes, but without reproducing between each other.

We have good reason to suppose that among the genes of today's living beings, the genes that once played an active role in the evolution of their species are still present. The existence, for example, of rudimentary organs that constitute relics of what were once fully developed organs indicates that the corresponding gene has survived down to the present day. This does not mean, however, that it is able to induce the formation of the entire organ (such is the case of the equidae, and of the four-winged drosophilae whose special feature represents something of a monstrosity.) We may well ask whether there is a repressive genetic system which phases out the ancestral genes that generate certain characteristics in special cases, for paleontological studies have not indicated a possible re-emergence of vanished organs.

Even before our knowledge of the genes enabled us to envisage the creation of hybrid forms by crossing two different species or to attempt other kinds of chromosomic manipulations, observations indicated that in the case of vertain vegetals, it was possible to arrive at a new species through interbreeding. In 1928, Karpechenko created the cabbage-radish, a form which possesses the chromosomes of both vegetals. Most of these newly formed vegetals are infertile, but there have been a few examples whose seeds contained a double number of chromosomes and which were indeed fertile, although only within the limits of this new species. While it is possible to induce the doubling of the chromosomes in certain vegetals, the same does not apply in the animal kingdom. There can be no hybridization between two lineages; zoology and paleontology do not provide a single example of this.

Genes and Regeneration

Examples of regeneration indicate beyond a shadow of a doubt the extraordinary capacity the genes possess for triggering the growth of new tissue after major amputations and even following the division of a body into several segments, such as we find in certain species.

In our discussion of regeneration, however, we shall not enter into detail on the subject of the tremendous capacity that certain organs in the mammals (man included) contain for development after an amputation : The liver is just one example among many of an organ which is perfectly able to regenerate, and the intestine is another. In the case of the latter, the mucosa is produced without difficulty to ensure the healing of a wound after the two segments have been surgically stitched together.

What concerns us here is regeneration that goes beyond the scope of the organs. In the case of certain animals, it affects localized segments of the body, which, when amputated, provoke the renewed development of the section removed. The triton is an example of this : Like other batrachians, when its muzzle, crest, tail, limbs or even its eyes are removed, the part that has disappeared is *entirely* reconstituted. The earthworm is another well-known example of regeneration : The anterior part of the worm containing the head will be replaced providing it is not cut at a point too far behind a clearly defined section of the body, and similarly the posterior part will reform providing the worm is not sliced at a point too far forward.

Examples of total regeneration are present among the inverte-brates. In certain cases, the animal is entirely reformed from a single segment of the body—*any segment*. In animals that figure lower down on the scale of organization, there are many common examples, such as the water hydra : The process of regeneration reconstitutes a number of new hydra that is equal to the number of segments into which the hydra has been cut. This animal also renews its tissues spontaneously in the course of its life. The most spectacular reconstitutions, however, take place in the bodies of the planarians and the nemertians. These are flat worms which possess a digestive tract. The planarian, which is anywhere between one and two centimetres long, can be carved into three parts by two transversal cuts, for example : Ten days later, three new worms will have formed. A regenerative 'bud' grows in the section left exposed by cutting, and in that bud, muscles, digestive and glandular tissues nerves, etc. begin to appear which will gradually replace all the missing organs in each of the three sections, brains and eyes included.

Even more extraordinary is the case of the nemertians; these are another variety of worm measuring some 20 centimetres to one metre in length. Like the planarians, the nemertians also regenerate, but they possess the added ability to cut themselves into segments (autotomy), an ability which is more highly developed than in other species. Autotomy is a defense mechanism used by an animal that is under attack. In such cases, the animal separates itself from the part of its body that has been caught by its attacker (the lizard leaves behind its tail, the crab jettisons its pincer) and that part subse-quently reforms. The nemertian goes further than this, however. As P.-P. Grassé writes in his 'Précis de biologie animale' *[Handbook of Animal Biology]*, when the nemertian undergoes a "brutal shock, whether chemical or mechanical, it spontaneously cuts itself transversally into sections which subsequently constitute new indi-viduals. Furthermore, when completely deprived of food, it is able to survive through an extraordinary process of involution. Its cells devour each other, and the organism gradually shrinks. Dawydoff has been able to obtain examples of *Lineus Lacteus* measuring 100 μ [i.e. one tenth of a millimetre] and composed of one dozen cells! P.-P. Grassé does not state whether the tiny number of cells that still remain are able to reconstitute an entire worm, but the performance of these animals remains all the same quite staggering.

However that may be, while the anatomy of the worm indicates regeneration processes triggered by the remains of the differentiated cells contained in the anterior part of a carved segment, it is not possible to talk of regeneration from these same vestiges when they are located in the posterior extremity (i.e. the tail end.) We are obliged to admit that throughout the body of the animal, from one end to the other, various cells are distributed that have a specialized regenerative function. Such cells are called 'neoblastic cells', and they constitute a kind of 'reserve pool' of embryonic cells which, by a process of differenciation, reconstitute all the tissues and organs.

What a remarkable wonder of organization this is! It is difficult to imagine the wealth of information that must be recorded on the D.N.A. molecules in the genes in order to arrive at such results at *exactly the right moment,* in other words at the moment circumstances bring all the appropriate mechanisms into play (such as the cutting of the worm into several distinct parts.) All these events take place in perfect order, and, lo and behold, ten days later the planarians have reconstituted themselves into normal individuals again! The autotomy of the nemertians is another marvel of organization, for these animals can divide themselves into sections under the effect of a specific stimulus. The genes which govern all these *perfectly coordinated actions* (this cannot be repeated often enough) within the cell and which set in motion the process of reconstruction, are genes that under normal conditions lie dormant. Phenomena such as these raise extremely complex genetic problems; they open the door to the question of the normal existence of 'inoperative' genes, or 'adaptative' genes, in other words genes that make adaptation possible.

Genes and Animal Behaviour

The behaviour of familiar animals and the often quite spectacular exhibition of certain abilities shown by others has led many people to attribute to these animals powers of reasoning that far exceed their real capabilities. Many animals do indeed give the impression that they are able to think through a certain situation and come to a decision which causes them to act with apparent logic. In fact however, a large number of animal activities are hereditary; the extent of automatic behaviour varies according to the degree of structural complexity of the species.

A particular outside situation can cause a stimulus in the more highly developed species, which the animal in question integrates into its 'memory bank', and which subsequently conditions its response. Some people think that this capacity is very closely akin to human faculties, but we shall see later on the very considerable difference between human behaviour and that of even the most highly developed animals. The difficulty arises from the fact that we are inclined to judge animals in terms of our own mental faculties, whereas we ought to judge them in terms of the faculties of the animals themselves.

The beings that are lowest on the scale of the invertebrates are capable only of automatism. A certain amount of information needed to induce and condition animal reactions is kept in the D.N.A. molecules, part of the genetic code. Chemical reactions continually occur as the environment changes : It is to these that the animal owes its behaviour.

A further degree of complexity appears when the activity concerned is cyclical or regular, interspersed with periods of rest. The building of nests by insects is an example of this. We see the same complexity present in the automatic act of stinging : The female mosquito invariably obeys an inner impulse when the stimuli are present that provoke heat and humidity on the human skin, especially when the mosquito smells the odour of butyric acid present in infinitely small quantities on the skin's surface. Here again, it is a case of innate behaviour; the appropriate information is registered in the genetic code of the species–the animal is simply obeying orders like a robot.

Nevertheless, some invertebrates are capable of conditioned reflexes. We should bear in mind that as opposed to the unconditioned reflex–where the involuntary action results from a single stimulus–, we are dealing here with a conditioned reflex which requires some 'preparation', as it were, before it can take place. At an initial stage, the real stimulus is associated with an accompanying neutral stimulus. In the second phase, the animal responds in the same way to the neutral stimulus alone. Reflexes such as this are present in bees and butterflies for example, where the animal is guided by the shape and colour of the flowers from which it gathers nectar; in the case of the bees, scent also plays a part. This is as far as the 'learning process' of these insects actually goes, however, for it is not possible to tame or train insects.

The vertebrates are the only animals capable of acquiring reflexes such as these and of recording and making use of information from the outside. Mammals can be trained; dogs are a particularly characteristic example, on account of their ability to integrate into human society. Here again, however, innate behaviour still persists, such as courting patterns, the preparation of various habitations which often requires very complex techniques, the raising of young, the marking-out of territory for defense purposes, the search for food, sexual relations, etc.

As the level of organization rises, innate behaviour persists, even though the animal is able to alter its response according to the given situation. Even in the case of the higher mammals, such as the primates, the automatic, invariable response dictated by the genetic code merely diminishes; it does not disappear completely. P.-P. Grassé provides two very important examples of this : Chimpanzees that have not lived in a forest since the day they were born, when set free, know exactly how to build a night shelter in the trees. They put together a kind of habitation that is identical to the dwellings constructed by chimpanzees that have lived all their lives in the natural environment of their species. Similarly, gorillas are always terrified by the sight of snakes in their native forests : The same reaction occurs in young gorillas faced by the sight of a dead snake, even though they are seeing a snake *for the very first time*. These are undoubtedly examples of innate behaviour : The animal is obliged to react in a certain way because it possesses in its D.N.A. molecules the gene or genes that induce the coded responses to the specific stimulus.

Perhaps one of the most spectacular examples of an animal capable of 'memorizing' or 'stockpiling' the information contained in the genetic code is the case of a bird native to Australia. The extraordinary migratory pattern of this particular bird is described in a work by J. Hamburger entitled 'La Puissance et la Fragilité' *[Power and Fragility]* [1] :

"On May 27, 1955, a Japanese fisherman caught a bird which was marked with a ring on March 14 of that same year on the Australian island of Babel. In that part of the world, the bird is known as the 'mutton-bird' or 'short-tailed shearwater.' The catch was the first of a series of discoveries leading to the reconstitution of the immense tour that this migratory bird undertakes every year. Its point of departure is the coast of Australia; from there, it flies east into the Pacific, turns north along the coast of Japan until it reaches the Bering Sea, where it rests for a while. After this halt, it sets off again, this time toward the south, hugging the west coast of America until it reaches California. From there it flies back across the Pacific to its starting point. This annual voyage of some 15,000 miles in the shape of the figure 8 never varies, either in terms of the route covered or the dates involved : The journey lasts six months and always comes to an end during the 3rd. week in September on the same island and in the

1. Published by Flammarion, Paris, 1972.

same nest that the bird left six months previously. What follows is even more curious : On their return, the birds clean their nests, mate, and lay their single egg during the ten last days in October. Two months later, the young chicks hatch out, grow rapidly, and at the age of three months watch as their parents fly away on their enormous journey. Two weeks later, around mid-April, the young birds take wing in their turn. *Without any guidance on the way,* they follow the exact same route described above. The implications of this are clear : Within the material transmitting their hereditary characteristics contained in the egg, these birds must possess all the directions required for such a journey. While some people may argue that these birds are guided by the sun and the stars, or by the winds prevailing along the route covered by their round-trip, such factors clearly do not account for the geographical and chronological precision of the voyage. There can be no doubt that whether directly or indirectly, the instructions for this 15,000-mile journey are recorded in the command-giving chemical molecules located within the nuclei of the cells of these birds. »

How is it possible to imagine the colossal mass of coded information that must of necessity be adapted to a host of different conditions, all of which take account of the various environments through which the birds must pass *alone and unguided*–from Australia to the Bering Sea and back again– while at the same time respecting a staggeringly precise timetable? How can we even begin to conceive of the fantastic number of orders that must be issued in the space of six months, orders that inevitably change according to circumstances, especially as the climate alters? *Every possible contingency must be anticipated within the total fund of information held by the D.N.A.* One wonders how the programme originally came to be written, and whether there is a being who knows the answer.

In today's computer age, such questions of programming cannot fail to make us think of some of man's own material achievements in recent years. We are filled with admiration for the magnificent technological results obtained by the American space shuttle which having completed its test flight, returned to earth at the moment calculated in advance. As scientific observers have repeatedly stressed, the launching of the shuttle, its orbiting around the earth, its descent back to earth, and many other manœuvres, were aided by powerful computers working in coordination. The computers issued orders to the shuttle's engines, and in certain instances rectified the original orders in accordance with positions which were themselves plotted by computer. In order for the venture to succeed, split-second timing was required for the recording of data, the processing of information, and the issuing of commands; an ensemble of operations that was far beyond any human capacity. Although piloted by two spacemen, the shuttle relied on pre-recorded information to complete each and every manœuvre. Our Australian 'mutton-bird' would have had as much difficulty completing its lone voyage for the first time across unknown continents and seas as the astronauts would have had in completing their mission, had it not been for the back-up supplied by information recorded in advance. In its genetic inheritance, the 'mutton-bird' simply *has* to possess all the instructions required for its six-month journey. Surely there is no-one naive enough to imagine that the space shuttle and all its computers could have been built and fed with highly complex programmes by the effect of mere chance? Anyone who thinks that has obviously lost touch with reality. In actual fact, the shuttle is programmed by highly trained experts who supply all the information required for its missions. Why should we not therefore accept the idea that the 'mutton-bird' –just as much as the space shuttle–must of necessity be put in possession of the information it requires in order to return to its point of departure? This is the logical conclusion we must draw from our comparison with the programmer.

Genetic Manipulations

Although this is a subject that affects man's future rather than his past, and although genetic mutations are 'experimental' and offer nothing in terms of the origins of man, they must be mentioned here on account of the legitimate anxiety they provoke.

The genes are responsible for each and every function of the cells. Some scientists have had the idea of supplying the cells with new properties by modifying the genes. In actual fact, they began by experimenting on organisms with a structure that is even simpler than the cell, namely the bacteria. By 'grafting' various genes onto Colon Bacilli, they triggered the production of certain therapeutic and nutritional substances; owing to the rapid reproduction of bacteria, they were able to obtain very large quantities of these substances. The experiment was particularly successful in the case of several hormones.

From this, it was suggested that experiments might be performed on more highly developed animals with the unspoken idea of creating new characteristics by 'grafting' new genes or modifying existing genes. Some scientists have even thought that, should these experiments prove successful, they might be applied to human genetics, in order to 'improve' man...

The above would imply a perfect familiarity with the genetic map of the D.N.A. tape, which is not the case at all. We may therefore assume that experimental successes of any importance within the animal kingdom are not likely to occur just yet. The extremely complex problems that remain to be solved would probably protect humanity from experiments such as these, but we must fear the worst as far as innovations deriving from human ingenuity are concerned : Man is capable of the worst as well as the best.

In an instance of this kind, man's dominance over man could reach to absolutely abominable extremes. The consequences of such practices, if they ever became feasible, are chilling indeed, for it is not difficult to imagine the abuses that would follow.

Nevertheless, these are precisely the practices currently being put forward by certain scientists. E. O. Wilson and the sociobiologists, whose theories have already been mentioned in connection with neo-Darwinism, have used their position as scientists to assume the right to organize human society in terms of their own theories, relying on genetic manipulations which they euphemistically label 'genetic engineering.' In their published works, they outline the process by which, in their view, new human beings could be produced. For example, in order to increase man's sense of family, what simpler solution would there be than to contribute the corresponding gene found in certain gibbons? Among these apes, there are certain individuals who are endowed with a distinctive anatomical characteristic which, more than in other apes of the same species, displays this highly developed sense. All that would have to be done, would be to 'graft' the characteristic onto man by means of the appropriate genetic supply. Suppose we wanted to increase people's enthusiasm for work : The simple transfer to us of the gene that conditions this function in worker bees would automatically turn us into total 'workaholics.'

The above examples of genetic manipulations, which were put forward by Wilson and his followers, were reported at a round-table conference on May 26, 1981 at the Palais de la Découverte in Paris. On the same occasion, brilliant papers were delivered on the subject by eminent scholars, among them P. Thuillier and P.-P. Grassé, while several of their colleagues commented on the extreme seriousness of the proposed projects. It would indeed be most unwise to treat lightly the proposals suggested above, for they are put forward by genuine experts who declare that by *virtue of their superior position as scientists, they have the right to change their fellow men as and how they please,* using procedures over which they alone have jurisdiction. This new 'master race' of scientists is also able to take advantage of the tremendous media coverage open to their theories in the United States. During the round-table conference at the Palais de la Découverte, P. Thuillier noted that sociobiology was gradually becoming institutionalized in France. It is indeed difficult at present to see how the sociobiologists can arrive at a technique for 'grafting' genes that are not yet isolated. But if they were one day able to isolate these genes and thereby realize projects which put man in the same category as laboratory animals, the abominable extremes at present feared would become a reality.

Let us not forget the extent of the scientific aberrations and contempt for man that, in the long run, were caused by Darwinism.

CREATIVE EVOLUTION

The term 'creative evolution' is not intended to carry any philosophical connotation in the sense in which it is used here. It is not often employed by modern scientists as a way of describing evolution, perhaps because the reference to 'creation' might come as a shock to the true researcher for whom the term suggests the idea of transcendence. In view of the facts described in the preceding pages however, it seems to me that we are simply stating a primordial truth when we use the term to qualify evolution in the animal kingdom. Indeed, *we must accept the facts as they are,* for when taken as a whole, evolution in the animal kingdom does not provide any possibility for a return to more ancient forms; complex structures do not revert to a simpler state. Quite the opposite happens in fact. Thus we are forced to take account of new forms that develop in the course of time, forms which are non-transitional, and which contain new organs that condition new functions. We may therefore talk of *the creation of organisms that did not previously exist,* either in terms of forms or functions.

In the latter case, the example of the Australian 'mutton-bird' is extremely revealing : Its migratory performances alone tell us that at a certain moment, the information required for the bird to undertake its fantastic journey must have been introduced into its genetic code. The informational data specific to the bird's organs must necessarily have been recorded in a genetic code that contained the specifications for all birds, at a time therefore when the birds were already in existence, i.e. after their emergence from a certain category of reptiles, some 135 million years ago.

Evolution as we know it is quite obviously dependent on a process of *successive additions of information over the course of time.* Scientists can argue ad infinitum about the causes determining the fact, but they cannot get away from the fact itself because it is patently obvious. Theories such as 'random genetic mutations' and the 'necessity of natural selection' may represent a satisfactory explanation of the past for some, but for others they are nothing more than unacceptable or half-baked hypotheses. It is blindingly clear, however, that the phenomena of evolution each had their beginnings marked by particular events.

When certain of today's theorists (who claim to have an explanation for everything) are asked just where the point of departure or origin of genetic information lies, they are at a loss for words. How could they fail to be? J. Monod has already acknowledged this inability to explain in the passage quoted earlier from his book 'Le Hasard et la Nécessité' *[Chance and Necessity]* : "The major problem is the origin of the genetic code and the mechanism by which it is expressed. Indeed, one cannot talk so much of a 'problem' as of a genuine enigma." We have started with an 'enigma', passed on to 'fortuitous mutations' which modify structures, and ended up with the 'necessity of natural selection', and not one of these theories has told us anything. They have not explained how highly organized matter came to be formed, complete with informational data to control its functioning and reproduction; nor have they enlightened us as to the complexity of the system which controls each and every aspect of the behaviour of entire organisms, as in the cases mentioned above.

Once we begin with complete objectivity to sort through the various ideas expressed on animal evolution by specialists from disciplines as disparate as the natural sciences, paleontology, molecular biology and genetics, the discrepancies become very striking. If we continue to remain impartial, we shall be forced to admit two facts : while there are paleontologists who take account of the data provided by the natural sciences, there are few specialists in molecular biology or genetics who turn to zoology, botany or paleontology to support their theories. In contrast to this, there are highly experienced specialists in the natural sciences, such as P.-P. Grassé, who constantly refer to the data supplied by chemistry and ultra-microscopic studies of the cell in their interpretation of the salient features of evolution. I turn once again to the data used by P.-P. Grassé to uphold and spread his concept of evolution, in which he tries to separate established fact from unproven speculation.

We have already examined the reasons why the theories of Lamarck and Darwin do not provide an explanation for the genesis of the basic phyla, each of which arrived at an organizational plan for an entire lineage. Fortuitous mutations do not adequately account for the emergence of major variations : They cannot create new forms with modifications that affect several organs in a coherent manner. All of these events took place in very long stages; at the beginning, there appeared the first signs of particular features, followed by a period of accentuation of these phenomena, which was rounded off by a phase during which events slowed down and the creation of new types finally ground to a halt. At the present time ('present' meaning at this point on a scale of millions of years), we would appear to be in this final stage. As we shall see later on however, in the case of man, evolution came to a halt much more recently.

All the major organizational types were laid down at a very early stage. From the moment a type engendered certain forms that oriented themselves in a particular direction, no new organizational types emerged from specialized forms. "Creative evolution has its roots in prototype forms; without them, no new types of organization can ever appear" (P.-P. Grassé).

The last great wave of evolution in fact took place during the early stages of the tertiary era with the emergence of the birds 135 million years ago. From that time onward, the amplitude of the variations diminished, until there were virtually none at all at the time man appeared. As for the causes of the variations in the speed of the process and the halt in the creation of new types, no-one knows the answer.

At the cellular level, evolution raises questions which can now be answered by molecular biology and genetics. No new phenomenon can occur in the cell without the intermediary of the D.N.A. molecule, which, by means of the R.N.A. molecule, is responsible for the formation of a protein that constitutes the origin of a chemical synthesis. For every important morphological variation, the D.N.A. molecule must acquire a new gene, thus adding to its fund of chemically held information, or modifications must occur in a gene that already exists. P.-P. Grassé was the first to put forward the idea that evolution could be explained by the creation of new genes. In his book, 'L'Evolution du vivant' *[The Evolution of Living Organisms]*, he quotes the statements of the American geneticist Ohno, who in 1970 said much the same thing. It has not of course been possible to demonstrate the formation of new genes over the course of time. Nevertheless, we shall see in a moment why it is unthinkable that this formation did not take place.

The acquisition of new information by living organisms is broadly outlined by P.-P. Grassé in the following passage :

"The responses to the stimuli conditioning evolution are recorded in the individual's genetic inheritance; this is what makes adaptation possible. Certain conditions must be present for these responses to be recorded. Now we know for certain–and this is a fact to bear in mind–that evolution diminished as the living world grew older. It is vain to ask, however, why these responses became more and more infrequent, for the present state of knowledge can provide no answer. Perhaps one day, when molecular biology is more refined and precise, we may find a reply to these questions.

"We do however possess certain facts which, while they may not solve the problem of evolution, at least enable us to gain a better understanding of the phenomena it entails, and thus help us direct our research into hitherto unexplored regions.

"An animal would not be in a position to survive if it had no information about its environment, taking the word in its widest sense. The sensory organs receive messages and transmit them in modified form to the nervous centres where they are interpreted and thereby trigger responses appropriate to outside stimuli. Acting as the 'computers' of the organism and capable of receiving various programmes, the nervous centres function in accordance with the specific and innate information that permanently controls their actions.

"The specific information lies within each cell, recorded on its D.N.A. tapes and contained in the genetic code. It is the intelligence of the entire species, which finds its material expression in an extremely miniaturized form. It is also the intelligence of the lineage at a particular time 'T' in evolution. The information settles on the D.N.A. tape into which it is integrated and recorded during the stages through which the successive species pass. It is the result of a slow process of development, during which a balance was struck between the living organism and its environment.

"Specific information is transmitted in the form of chemical signals emitted by the segments or genes in the D.N.A.

"Nevertheless", as P.-P. Grassé stresses, "the formation of new genes has not been observed by a single biologist; and yet without that formation, evolution becomes an inexplicable phenomenon."

P.-P. Grassé completes his theory in the following manner :

"In our opinion, new information, which materializes and integrates itself permanently into the genetic code in the form of sequences of nucleotids, can only arise from preliminary intracellular reactions. It has nothing whatsoever to do with mistakes in the copying process or anomalies in the D.N.A. : It is in fact the result of an orderly development that takes place over successive generations. The evolutionary process operates when very precise conditions are present; for the moment, those conditions do not appear to arise very often. The moving forces behind this remarkable process are most probably stimuli received from outside, internal impulses, and the general responses of the organism which affect it right down to the level of the molecule."

The main theories we have passed in review may be narrowed down to two hypotheses : The theory of mutations resulting from 'errors in the copying process' of the genetic code, the product of chance, with the possible control of corrective procedures such as natural selection or other factors; and the theory of creative evolution, which cannot unfortunately be based on a demonstration of the existence of new genes. Even though the material recording of new information in the genes remains to be shown, there can be no doubt that the concept of new data as the determining factor of evolution provides a perfect explanation for the phenomena observed.

So which of the two theories do we choose?

a) The theory which relies on the basic role of chance is untenable for the reasons we have already discussed.

b) The theory based on creative evolution via new information is perfectly logical. Its validity is clearly illustrated by P.-P. Grassé in his book 'Précis de biologie générale' *[Handbook of General Biology]* :

"If we deny the formation of new genes, what we are in fact saying is that the Amoeba or the Monera [1], as Haeckel would have expressed it, possessed all the genes which, in the course of evolution, were distributed among the various species in the animal kingdom.

"This mystical conception of the living world, in which everything is considered to be preformed, comes as a shock to any biologist who sets great store by reason and scientific precision. How can one seriously acknowledge that the most primitive living being could *genuinely and substantially* have contained within itself all the genes of the animal kingdom, or even the vegetable kingdom, without thereby lapsing into tacit animism?

"The acquisition of genes is the absolute prerequisite for evolution. We cannot avoid this possibility, for our whole comprehension of evolution and its inmost mechanisms depends on it, and it alone."

Jean Rostand does not appear to have been perturbed by the term 'creative evolution'. This celebrated biologist has never made any

---

1. Author's note : a primitive unicellular organism, which, according to Haeckel, did not possess a nucleus.

secret of his materialistic ideas. Let us therefore conclude the first part of the present book with a quotation from him on the opposed theories of creative evolution, and chance and necessity :

"I have only to watch a cricket leap or a dragonfly dart through the air, in order to feel more akin to Pierre-P. Grassé than to Jacques Monod."

II

THE EVOLUTION OF MAN
COMPARED WITH
THAT OF OTHER LIVING BEINGS :
SIMILARITIES AND DIFFERENCES

THE SUCCESSIVE WAVES OF HUMAN TYPES:
FROM PRIMITIVE MAN TO HOMO SAPIENS

If we apply the same criteria to man as to the rest of the animal kingdom, his anatomical characteristics would seem at first glance to place him in the order of primates that gave birth to the lineages containing present-day apes. As P.-P. Grassé has stressed, however, the ancient forms of these lineages have still not been discovered. We are faced with an enormous gap in our knowledge.

"In the history of the primates, we must be careful not to take at face value the reconstitutions of our ancestors based on on a few scanty vestiges (some teeth, a fragment of jawbone, the top of a skull) which were put forward in all seriousness by highly imaginative paleontologists. This explains why genealogical trees of Man are quickly devised, and just as quickly discarded. The most recent works on the subject appear to be fairly mediocre, even though they concern new and interesting discoveries; the researchers engaged in these studies have neither the knowledge nor the good sense to interpret the discoveries correctly."

What is striking in many publications is the existence of a very strong wish to announce the reconstitution of a man dating from an age that is even older than that of the oldest man so far discovered. To achieve this, insignificant debris are used which by no means lead to certainties. Exaggerated claims resulting from imaginative interpretations in this field are legion.

One of the latest discoveries concerning the oldest man yet known is the *Ramapithecus*. It was found in India and Kenya in sediments dating from the tertiary era, around fifteen million years ago. The fossil in question (which is in fact limited to a few vestiges of bones) cannot seriously be integrated into the ancestry of man. According to P.-P. Grassé: "Even if one had the genius of Cuvier, one could not reconstruct an animal from a few bits of debris." Whatever certain observers may say, therefore, these modest remains do not represent an ancestor of man.

The same applies to another so-called ancestor, *the Oreopithecus*, which is in fact a fossilized ape : The animal clearly lived in the forest, for its arms are very long–much longer than its lower limbs–as is the case for apes which swing from tree to tree. It is roughly twelve million years old, very small in size in comparison with today's man (1.10 metres to 1.20 metres), and its cranial capacity is quite small (400 cc.) As in the case of the Ramapithecus, the fossilized remains are not accompanied by any sign of activity that might be considered human. E. Genet-Varcin puts the Oreopithecus in an independant family, for she does not consider that it can be the ancestor of the hominids that were to follow.

Given the present state of knowledge, there seems to be general agreement that the *Australopithecus* is a specimen that belongs to the most ancient wave of authentic hominids who lived, not in the forest like the great apes, but in the savannah. The first example of this type was discovered in South Africa in 1924, and other remains were subsequently unearthed in the same region. More recently, vestiges come from near the great African Lakes (Leakey, 1959.) Remains may also have been found in Java in sediments that are possibly one to four million years old. Some observers think that a form of Australopithecus, called *Meganthropus* because it is larger than the others, was found in Java in terranes dating only from 600,000 years ago. They probably belong to the type in question, even at this era, but doubts remain and we cannot state for sure that this first great ancestor of man lived until this time.

We must also mention the fact that French paleontologists, among them Y. Coppens, have discovered remains of the Australopithecus in terranes between one and four million years old. The discoveries were first made in 1967 in the Omo Valley in Ethiopia. The fossilized remains of a woman in her twenties, subsequently named 'Lucy' were discovered in 1974 in the Afar, in sediments that date from 3.5 million years ago.

The specimens are generally small in size : One type might measure roughly 1.5 metres, another, more slender specimen, could measure some 1.25 metres. The skeleton of the face presents ape-like features. The skull sometimes displays a sagittal crest. In these specimens, however, characteristics are present that are undeniably human : The biped posture, the curvatures of the spine, which resemble those of man on account of the protuberance of the fifth lumbar vertebra, the broad pelvis, the femur, which is adapted to the biped posture, the anterior position of the foramen magnum or occipital foramen (large opening in the basal part of the skull through the occipital bone.) The dentition also displays human characteristics : The teeth are small at the front, but the premolars and molars are very large.

While its cranial capacity remained small (roughly 500 to 550 cc.), the Australopithecus was capable of thought, and of using tools which he fashioned himself. Among the sites containing human fossils, pebbles have been found that were fashioned so as to form a cutting edge; they were probably used for hunting. These sharpened flints indicate a capacity for invention and creation that is not possessed by the apes. Such qualities enabled the Australopithecus to produce even more sophisticated implements which he held in his fist or used as a small hatchet. He also fashioned tools made of split bone, employing a technique that allowed him to use the implements as daggers and clubs (R.A.Dart.) The discovery of animal bones, in particular the bones of antelopes, suggest that the Australopithecus also hunted these animals. There is no trace of a fireplace in any of the excavated sites. These are the most relevant aspects of the details provided by E. Genet-Varcin on these ancestors of men, and the men who were to follow.

The second wave of hominids were the *Pithecanthropines* or *Archanthropians*.

A Dutch military doctor, named Eugène Dubois, is said to have requested a post in Indonesia in the hope of finding there what he thought was the 'missing link' between the apes and man. In 1890, he discovered in Java the top of a cranium, and a femur which seemed to display human characteristics. Not until 1936, however, were further fossils of the same type discovered in Java, identical to the specimen named by Dubois *Pithecanthropus Erectus*. A large quantity of remains of a type later called *Sinanthropus* were uncovered between 1928 and 1937 in the Chou Kou Tien Caves near Peking. Over the last twenty years, remains have been excavated by L.S.B. Leakey in Tanzania, Y. Coppens in Chad, and vestiges have been found in Asia and Indonesia. E.Genet-Varcin is doubtful about discoveries of this type of man in Europe, but P.-P. Grassé classes among the Pithecanthropines the Tautavel Man, which was discovered near Perpignan in France. The human remains found in the Lazaret Caves in Nice, and those uncovered at Ternifine in the Oran region of Algeria also seem to P.-P. Grassé to belong to the same type. He thinks that the Pithecanthropines may have lived some 500,000 years ago, surviving for roughly 350,000 years.

At this point, man seems to have grown in size : Interpretations of the skeletal fragments uncovered indicate heights between 1.58 metres and 1.78 metres, depending on the site in which the remains were found. The human characteristics of these remains are quite marked, and the upright posture can be discerned.

The average cranial capacity is roughly 900 cc. (in a range of 775 to 1,200 cc.) A bony protuberance is always present above the eye-sockets (orbits), and on the back of the head. The orbits are extremely large. The general look of the face resembles the human types that were later to follow.

From the time of the Australopithecus, intellectual powers began to develop. The Pithecanthropus used fire, as indicated by the discovery in the Chou Kou Tien Caves of burnt animal bones, and stones blackened by fire arranged in a circle. The Pithecanthropus, shows a more sophisticated ingenuity than the Australopithecus, as evidenced by discoveries both in China and in Tanzania. We find this again in Europe at Tautavel near Perpignan, where H. de Lumley uncovered scrapers and pointed implements. In the Lazaret Caves in Nice, there are traces of picks driven into the ground and stones arranged in rows which may have marked the limits of various habitations. All these discoveries indicate a certain capacity for reasoning and reflection.

In comparison with modern man however, the Australopithecus and the Pithecanthropus possessed a very small brain. This is an important point, for in all likelihood, there is a direct link between the volume of the brain and the development of its functional capacity, which is conditioned by the number of neurones present. Today, a person whose brain ceases to develop once it attains a volume of less than 1,000 cc. will most probably show signs of mental retardation that prevent him from leading a normal life. The first two waves of hominids possessed a brain volume of less than 1,000 cc., and yet they displayed powers of invention and creation. P.-P. Grassé considers that : "This proves the rule whereby the various states through which a lineage passes during its development must be functional, balanced and irreversible. The Australopithecus and the Pithecanthropus, each with their respective brain capacities of 500 cc. and 800 cc., lived and prospered in harmony with their environment, thus indicating the truth of the statement that evolution never takes place in abnormal or disorderly conditions."

The third wave of hominids were the *Neanderthals* (or *Paleanthropians.)* According to some sources, they appeared roughly 100,000 years ago and lived approximately 60,000 years. Other observers, such as E.Genet-Varcin, think that they appeared much earlier, perhaps as much as 500,000 years ago. The Neanderthals lived in Europe, Asia and Africa.

The first remains of Neanderthal Man were discovered in 1856 in the Neander Valley near Düsseldorf in West Germany. Not until 1908, however, was the first more or less complete skeleton uncovered at La Chapelle-aux-Saints in the Corrèze region of France. Later, identical types turned up in Spain, Italy, Greece, Morocco, Palestine, Iraq and Java.

Although Neanderthal Man was of medium size, perfectly biped, and endowed with well-developed muscles, his facial morphology was different from that of man today : His forehead was low, being reduced almost to a large bony protuberance above the orbits, and the absence of a chin gave his face a muzzle-like appearance. Compared with the hominids of the second wave, however, Neanderthal Man's skull is more developed : Its capacity increased at this point from 1,300 cc. to 1,600 cc. The development of his intellectual level is borne out by the quality of weapons and implements discovered near the remains of Neanderthal Man. He most probably found shelter in caves, in which he made fire and arranged his surroundings to suit his convenience.

It has been suggested by some paleontologists that the existence in burial sites of objects thought to be required in the afterlife (large pieces of animals, antlers and horns, stone implements) indicates a certain spirituality (?). The halo-like arrangement of antlers around the head of the deceased, and various deposits of ochre may likewise bear witness to a certain aesthetic sensibility (E.Genet-Varcin.)

One wonders whether Neanderthal Man gave birth to *Homo Sapiens*—the latter simply following on from the former—or whether they both coexisted side by side. Fossilized remains, such as the Qafzeh Man discovered in Palestine, possess a skull that is almost the same as that of Homo Sapiens, displaying only a very minor frontal protuberance (a feature that resembles Neanderthal Man); the coexistence of the two types may well have led to interbreeding. According to P.-P.Grassé, there are solid paleolontological arguments to support the idea of the coexistence some 100,000 years ago of Homo Sapiens and Neanderthal Man (the absence of the bony protuberance above the orbits, and the fact that the occipital foramen magnum is located very far forward are particularly important in this respect.) Does this therefore mean that we may talk of a *Praesapiens* type?

While the above is simply a hypothesis, there is reason to think that man as we know him today displayed these principal anatomical characteristics some 35,000 to 40,000 years ago, thus constituting the species known as Homo Sapiens :

The following is a brief summary of the data on Homo Sapiens supplied by E.Genet-Varcin :

Compared with the third wave of hominids, the fourth displays a higher, more spherical skull, with a well-developed occipital region; the bony protuberance above the orbits has disappeared, and, owing to the appearance of a chin, so has the muzzle-like aspect of the face. The cranial capacity has been reduced to an average of 1,350 cc., and the limbs have acquired the proportions we know today.

The first representatives of this latest wave were discovered in many parts of Europe, Asia and Africa. The best preserved and most accurately dated skeletons were found in France; for example, the Combe-Capelle Man, and in particular the Cro-Magnon Man, which was discovered in 1868 at Les Eyzies in the Dordogne region. The height of Cro-Magnon Man is greater than that of Combe-Capelle Man (1.80 metres), and he still possesses certain archaic features : The occipital region of the skull is not yet entirely developed, the face is very wide—but the orbits are situated at a lower position—and the nose is protuberant. These few remaining features were quickly to disappear, however, and thereafter, there were no noticeable changes in human morphology.

"From the moment he first appeared, *Homo Sapiens* displayed a degree of psychic activity superior to that of any hominid preceding him. He was able to sharpen stones with considerable skill, versatility, subtlety and aesthetic sensibility. He made great use of bone and ivory, no longer in their quasi-raw state, but fashioned into various tools : picks, awls, batons, implements for smoothing objects or casting projectiles, needles, tridents, harpoons, hooks, etc."... "His habitations... were quite varied. As in the past, when faced with a harsh climate, he found shelter in caves and rocks. In regions without natural shelters, he knew how to dig and prepare the ground, and to construct huts made of branches; traces of a fireplace indicate what was once the focal point of the habitation.

"Man lived as a predator-cum-gatherer; he hunted game and picked fruit, thus supplying himself with food and clothing. His skill as a hunter is evident from the remains of animals found at sites such as Solutré in the Saône-et-Loire region of France; he sometimes used these animal remains to furnish his home. In order to light his habitation, he knew how to choose wood that would burn without leaving much soot, and he also made use of stone lamps."

He "was able to create works of art, no genuine traces of which have ever been found from periods prior to him"... "Representations of animals form his main pictorial theme." Among other works of art, E.Genet-Varcin cites the cave-paintings at Altamira and Lascaux.

It is useful to remember that in the Altamira Caves near Santander in Spain, there are wall-paintings and engravings of bovines and cervidae which cannot easily be dated precisely. Various contents of the caves have been analysed by carbon 14 radiochronology, and an estimated figure of 13,500 years has been suggested. It is not possible, however, to be absolutely certain that the figure represents the age of the paintings themselves : Some estimates would seem to indicate that the works of art are much older. The Lascaux Caves in France are remarkable for the wide range of animals depicted and the variety of artistic skills employed. The paintings are thought to date from roughly the same period as those found at Santander, but here again, some observers think they may be even older.

In E.Genet-Varcin's opinion, the man of this period "displayed preoccupations of a metaphysical kind. The numerous burial grounds contain human remains that are often arranged in the foetal position, daubed with red ochre, decorated with ornaments fashioned into headdresses, necklaces, bracelets, and pendants, and composed of shells, teeth, and round pieces of bone. In the vicinity of the human body were placed stone weapons, the remains of animals, and the antlers of reindeer and stags. The body was surrounded by large slabs of stone, and sometimes even covered by them. "... "When it came to expressing his sentiments", the man of this period "attained a psychic level equal to that of modern man".

Although he subsequently underwent a few morphological variations, these changes only superficially affected man's organs and functions. Since heredity has continued these modifications right down to the days of recorded history, the concept of different *races* has been put forward. In fact, these were primarily entities that were initially grouped geographically, and within which dominant mutations occurred and were subsequently perpetuated. Various groups appeared prematurely which displayed distinctive characteristics, but they all retained the basic features of modern man. For example, P.-P.Grassé cites the 'Negroids' of Grimaldi (Monaco), the oldest 'race', the Cro-Magnon Man, European in type, and the Chancelade Man, whose kinship with the Mongoloid race is currently in dispute.

Very quickly, however, mixed characteristics began to appear in the various fossils uncovered, causing P.-P.Grassé to add the following note : "Racial purity is an entirely imaginary concept. It does not exist at present, if indeed it ever did exist. All men are hybrids derived from various races, but in differing degrees."

Studies of mutations which may perhaps grant certain very minor advantages to particular human groups indicate that man does not at present display any tendancy toward a new type of organization : For man, evolution has come to a halt.

EVOLUTION
IN THE VARIOUS HUMAN GROUPS

The Gaps In Our Knowledge

In the previous chapter, we provided a very broad and simplified summary of the data on the predecessors of man that arise from an objective, unbiased examination of scientific discoveries. From this summary, certain facts emerged that were patently clear : Next to the indisputable material for thought imposed by paleontology concerning periods which are in fact only roughly defined, there are equally indisputable *gaps in our knowledge,* in other words *places where links are missing.* In particular, these gaps concern the birth of the order of primates and the link with the three animal branches that descend from it. Almost the only material for study that we possess for these branches are the present-day forms of these animals. In actual fact, our knowledge of the most primitive hominid forms begins with the very recent Australopithecus; 'recent' because it is only one to five million years old (six million years old according to some), which in terms of evolution is not very old at all.

If we leave aside forms such as *Homo Erectus,* and *Homo Habilis,* which may be linked to the main waves of human types or may simply be forms very similar to those already mentioned, there would seem to be *four main waves* in the succession of hominids that appeared on earth [1]. Each wave displays a more developed structural organization compared with that of its predecessor, leading toward the appearance of the perfectly adapted final type. For example, primordial human features began to appear, such as the biped

1. This is the figure provided by the current state of knowledge. It by no means rules out the possibility of further waves that still remain to be discovered, nor does it exclude the addition of forms already known today but which may become more significant later on.

posture, the functions of the hand and articulate speech. These characteristics developed simultaneously with the growth of the intelligence and psychical powers (the expanded cranial capacity indicates the increasingly sophisticated organization of the brain.) This suggests a constant march toward greater organizational complexity : Each wave displays a progression in comparison with the one preceding it, as part of a decidedly discontinuous march which came to a halt roughly 35,000 to 40,000 years ago, according to today's calculations. The latter are subject to future revision, but it is highly unlikely that the experts responsible for determining the age of the terranes in which the fossils were found are far wrong in their estimates. Geochronology is based particularly on the measurement of the radioactivity of rock samples that contain radioelements : for example lead or strontium, or potassium-argon for the datation of specimens that are millions of years old, and radioactive carbon for samples no more than 50,000 years old.

It is important to bear in mind, however, that paleontology can only provide a fairly definitive estimate of the period in which a particular type lived when there are many samples present : Their existence in large numbers enables us to state that a certain form lived from point A in time to point B, but that does not rule out the possibility that remains exist which are as yet undiscovered, lying hidden in terranes that are perhaps older or younger than those under study. Unfortunately, as far as the most ancient ancestors of man are concerned, very few fossilized remains have so far been uncovered. Given the present state of knowledge, therefore, we must limit ourselves to stating that a certain form lived at a certain time, and we should be very wary when giving approximate dates for its possible appearance or disappearance.

Were the Waves Independent or Interdependent?

The major question facing us today is the nature of the links that may or may not have existed between the waves at present identifiable. We know for sure that man's functional and psychical powers—and in particular his creative intelligence—all developed at the same rate as certain of his anatomical features (cranial capacity, for example.) This development occurred with perfect regularity within the progress of time, and there is no evidence of any regression toward a less evolved form. In the light of these facts, there seems at first no reason why we should not apply the same rules to man as to the rest of the animal kingdom, thus allowing the four waves of

hominids to derive one from another in succession : From the
Australopithecus came the Pithecanthropus, which gave birth to
Neanderthal Man, the direct ancestor of *Homo Sapiens*—not to
mention various secondary branches.

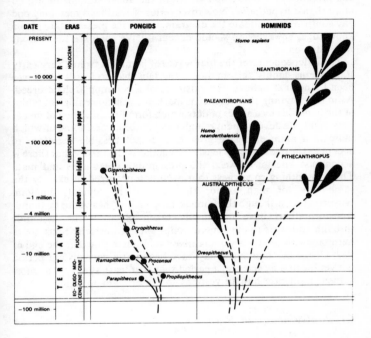

Simplified Diagram Showing the Phylogeny of the Hominids According to E. Genet-Varcin
(Encyclopaedia Universalis, volume 8, page 499)

As may be seen, E. Genet-Varcin considers that at the beginning of the tertiary era, some sixty
million years ago, the lineage that was to produce the great apes (shown on the left) and the
lineage that was lead to present-day man (indicated on the right) are quite separate from each
other. Even for periods prior to the tertiary era, there is no evidence to suggest the existence of
a common origin.

As a paleontologist, however E. Genet-Varcin finds that this
theory 'presents many difficulties.' It implies that the *four main
groups have probably existed independently of each other from a
very early stage*. The phylogeny (see diagram) of the hominids which
appears in the *Encyclopaedia Universalis* (volume 8, page 499),

indicates that the first three waves—which may share a common origin with the fourth—ceased to flourish one after the other, the third wave dying out some 40,000 years ago. The succession was continued by the fourth wave which gave birth to Cro-Magnon Man and present-day *Homo Sapiens*. All of the above statements are no more than a hypothesis : New discoveries of fossilized men may one day confirm or invalidate the diagram. Given the present state of our knowledge, however, we should accept it : We shall see the reasons why later on.

The independence of the four waves of hominids from a very early stage seems doubly certain due to the fact that no fossils have ever been found that indicate the existence of a common archaic breed. As in the diagram, this absence is marked on the genealogical tables of the hominids by a series of dots which form lines that do not meet : they mark the development of independant branches, some of which indicate a more extensive growth. It is not possible therefore to accept as the one and only feasible hypothesis the theory that there is a common lineage between the present-day great apes and man. There is nothing to suggest that evolution occurred in exactly the same way for man as for the rest of the animal kingdom. Nevertheless, although the famous 'missing link' has yet to be found, transformations have undeniably taken place in the hominids through additions to the genetic code. These transformations are in harmony with the theory of creative evolution outlined at the end of Part One. Thus humanity may have begun at a very distant period not yet located by science, a period that is at least as old as the most ancient authentic human vestiges so far brought to light.

Gradually Acquired Stability

For the reasons discussed in the preceding chapter, evolution of some kind undeniably occurred in the various human groups. It definitely seems to have come to a halt, however, shortly before the beginning of recorded history.

Since that time, in other words since the stage at which the form *Homo Sapiens* was reached, evolution does not seem to have continued to create. This stability was attained when man acquired a completely biped posture, with all the structural and other anatomical features that such a posture implies, and simultaneously, with the development of the brain as the cranial capacity expanded. Man's growing psychic powers and the development of his ability to perceive, reason and decide—all of which led to the loss of his automatic behavioural patterns—helped him in the course of tens of thousands of years to adapt to external circumstances.

As P.-P. Grassé has stated : "Man is one of the most cosmopolitan terrestrial animals; he can live in any part of the world. He has undergone several thousand different types of mutations, if we judge by the number of alleles [1] whose existence is proven by the variety to be found among human beings. There are currently [2] three billion two hundred million people in the word, all of whose genotypes are different (except for those of identical twins.) Consequently, there is an ample supply of people who can undergo mutations to fulfil the needs of natural selection. But what in actual fact is happening? The answer is that nothing of any importance is currently taking place, or at least nothing that is worth noting. The last anatomical feature acquired by man was the chin (which developed some 30,000 to 40,000 years ago, and probably earlier than that if we take into account *Homo Praesapiens*.)

"Mutations are what make one person different from another, and they perform this task extremely well. But as for the human species as a whole, the favourable conditions for evolution provided by the various human populations and the diversity of their habitats do not change the fact that man's present anatomical and physiological structure is stable.

"In every population, human individuals differ from each other according to their genotype. In spite of this, the species *Homo Sapiens* is undergoing no change whatsoever, either in its organizational plan, its structure, or its functions... Against a background of common features, an infinite number of differentiating and personalizing 'embellishments' appear, none of which has any value in terms of evolution."

The gradual progression towards stability is obvious.

The evolution of the human species was very rapid (a point to which we shall return), but that does not mean to say that it was sudden or abrupt. Each change resulted in modifications which mutually complemented one another in the course of time, both with regard to form as well as function. This fact is borne out by the progress made in terms of intelligence, reasoning and creation, as may be seen in the case of the increased skill with which stone was fashioned, as mentioned above.

1. Author's note : Alleles are mutations that take place at the genetic level.
2. This quotation is taken from 'Evolution du vivant' *[The Evolution of Living Organisms]*, published in 1973.

Fortuitous Variations
Do Not Provide An Answer

Too often, we tend to overlook the tiny number of human generations that separate the Australopithecus from *Homo Sapiens*. At a very generous estimate, roughly two million years passed between the end of the first wave of hominids and the fourth wave; if we view these notions in the light of theories currently upheld by some observers, we arrive at the following conclusions : Fortuitous mutations affected only one lineage, and natural selection or some other factor determined the role of chance, channelling its actions in the desired ultimate direction. In fact, however, we can quickly see how impossible this is; two million years represent some 80,000 generations of humans, and at the time, the human population of the world was very small, as evidenced by the rarity of fossils discovered. How can we imagine, therefore, that in such a short period of time and in such a tiny population, the mutations could have taken place that were necessary for the coordinated organization of cerebral development (complete with billions of neurones) in the final stage of the evolution of the brain? The above theory cannot possibly provide an explanation : P.-P. Grassé thinks it is 'absurd.' The evolution of the human species cannot be the result of chance, any more than that of the rest of the living world.

In contrast to this, however, man acquired many new attributes : We shall quickly see that simple references to the rest of the animal kingdom do not allow us to speak of fortuitous mutations or to suppose that these attributes were passed down from one generation to another.

THE MOST DEBATED ORIGIN:
THE APES OR THEIR ANCESTORS

*The Importance of Dealing
With This Subject*

In spite of certain gaps in our knowledge, the firmly established facts described in the preceding chapters allow us to think that we possess some extremely relevant data concerning the origins of man and the transformations that he underwent during the course of time. In addition to this, our knowledge of evolution in the animal kingdom may also supply insights on certain points concerning man, providing we make careful and objective use of the general ideas to be drawn from such data. It is of course a pity that the study of specimens that are visible to the naked eye (paleontology, zoology) contains gaps that we would naturally like to see filled. Without wishing to diminish in any way the importance of the contribution made by these disciplines, however, we must draw attention to the tremendous progress made in the comprehension of evolution due to the studies of the cell performed by molecular biology and genetics. Nevertheless, according to some of the most brilliant specialists in these disciplines, all the questions have been solved through the discoveries made by the most recent research (let us not forget J. Monod and the manner in which he set forth his infallible dogma!) In actual fact, by bringing to light certain aspects of cellular life through study at the molecular level, investigation has revealed the existence of the most formidable enigma as far as the organization of the living world is concerned : It consists in the origin of the genetic code which, as it subsequently developed, conditioned the course of all living beings, as noted in our discussion of creative evolution.

Unfortunately, there are far too few specialists in the basic sciences who have arrived at this conclusion. Most of them are more inclined to come to a hasty decision that squares with their own ideologies than to direct their attention to the precise point they are trying to solve; they strive to set forth ideas that tend constantly to 'animalize' man. As far as the spirit governing the approach to the problem is concerned, one is forced to wonder whether it has changed all that much since the time of Darwin. In practical terms, the discussion inevitably comes back to the same question : "Is man descended from the apes or at least from one of his close ancestors?" Many modern researchers convey the feeling that they are motivated by a need to reinforce an old theory with scientific arguments, providing us with a kind of 'update' that appeals to modern-day tastes. While the arguments themselves may not date from the time of Darwin, in the case of many researchers, the basic spirit shared by the first partisans of Darwin's theory (who were probably far more fanatical than the master himself) shows through with perfect clarity.

As for the controversies of the past, we must not forget the heated exchanges that took place, at the meeting of the British Association in 1860, between Bishop Wilberforce and Thomas Huxley. In reply to Wilberforce, who rejected the theory that man was descended from the apes, Huxley, as a defender of Darwinism, stated that he would rather be the descendant of an ape than the offspring of a human being who demolishes the work of a scientist championing the defence of truth.

These controversies, which were once limited to a small circle of experts, are now open to a very large public due to radio and television programmes; we are well aware of the tremendous impact these media possess compared with other forms of mass-communication. Sad to say, the language used in these media tends more often than not to 'animalize' man. That is why two particular programmes that appeared on French television came as such a surprise to me when I watched them : In speaking of subjects connected with biology and man, the head of an important research institute actually referred one day to 'divine genius' in connection with the genes. On another occasion, I listened to a former professor at the Sorbonne raise strong objections to theories which tend to turn us all into descendants of the apes. How unusual it is to hear ideas publicly expressed that contradict today's predominantly materialistic theories!

Those Presented As Our Grandparents

Later on, we shall examine the obvious differences between the apes and man; we shall refer to certain features present in each respective group, thus indicating that the existence of certain human attributes prevents us from sharing a common ancestry. First however, we must outline the origins of the apes and describe certain important features that concern them.

It is possible to suppose that some seventy million years ago there lived various species that were half-insectivorous and half-primatial, and which formed the origin of the lineage; there are very few fossilized remains, however. Specimens have been brought to light in terranes that are roughly thirty million years old, and these are said to represent the first forms of ape-like types. Many more examples from later periods have been discovered. We should note, however, that in referring to these various fossils, certain paleontologists mention forms that 'might have similarities to...', 'are likely to be linked to...', or 'seem to have given birth to...' a particular form that exists today.

This is indeed an indication of the uncertainty that pervades ideas concerning the origins of the apes. If we turn back to the preceding chapter, we shall see from E. Genet-Varcin's diagram of the lineages of the pongids and hominids that a few dots indicate the discovery of ancients forms, such as the Ramapithecus of the tertiary era, which was thought by some to be an ancestor of man. While we find that between four (or six) and one million years, the development of the first hominid considered at present to be such (the Australopithecus) is marked in right-hand column of the diagram (at a more recent period, Neanderthal Man), we find on the side devoted to the pongids a series of interrupted dots indicating uncertainties due to lack of fossilized forms discovered. Not until we reach the top of the 'Pongid' column do we find any development of forms similar to those known today. The latter may indeed have possessed distant precursors with forms indicated by the fossilized remains we have discovered from the tertiary era, it is however very difficult to reach any positive conclusions based on such meagre vestiges. Nevertheless, there are those who maintain that the great apes reached anatomical stability nine million years ago. If that were the case, however, the great apes would have been too 'mature' to give birth to the first human form—known today as the Australopithecus—which did not in fact appear until much later.

At this point, some people will immediately say that the pongids and hominids possessed a common ancestor. There is, however, not one single discovery to prove this. Nobody has succeeded in finding the form that provides the link between the two lineages indicated on the diagram. That is why they remain quite separate.

"It has been claimed that the human branch is an offshoot of an archaic form bearing ape-like features. This is by no means sure, however, for the oldest known primates already possess features indicating an adaptation specific to life in the trees. These features are not present either in the anatomy of man or that of the Australopithecus" (P.-P. Grassé). If this common branch had existed, a divergence would have occurred at a much earlier period than that of the appearance of the first apes. Thus we are left with nothing but conjectures. One thing is certain, however : Man could not have been formed at the cost of the evolved forms such as the pongids (chimpanzees, gorillas, orang-outangs, for example).

There are two extremely important characteristics common to all monkeys and apes (with a few very rare exceptions) : The fact that they live in the trees, and therefore possess extremely long and well-developed upper limbs, and the fact that they do not display a biped posture. The few species of monkeys and apes that do not climb trees but live in mountain regions still remain quadrupeds. As far as I know, the gibbons are the only species which occasionally displays a biped posture, but they nevertheless possess upper limbs that are long and well-developed. These two distinguishing features of the lineage composed of monkeys and apes are not present in man.

Similarities and Differences
Between the Anatomical Features of the Two Lineages

The general anatomical features of man and the great apes appear on first sight to possess striking similarities. There is no point in denying this fact. The structures present in the two lineages must be compared in much greater detail, however, than is afforded by a cursory examination of the obvious.

In this context, it is worth noting that some of Darwin's most ardent supporters—such as Thomas Huxley—were perfectly well aware of the evident differences that exist between man and the apes. As Huxley himself wrote : "I shall therefore take this opportunity plainly to state that, on the contrary, they are both considerable and significant; that every bone in the body of a gorilla bears a feature that distinguishes it from the corresponding bone in a human, and that, at least in creation today, no intermediary form bridges the gap separating man from the troglodyte."

The opinions of modern researchers seem to indicate the exact opposite, however, for they claim that 98 % of the genes present in the chimpanzee are shared by man (J. de Grouchy, 'De la naissance des espèces aux aberrations de la vie' [*From the Birth of the Species to the Abnormalities of Living Forms*].) [1].

General inventories have been compiled listing the purely anatomical characteristics of the great apes as compared with those of man. One such inventory was drawn up by A. Keith, who in 1915 set out to study all the possible anatomical features that might be shared by man and various species of apes : The chimpanzees and gorillas were found to be more or less related, according to the study, while the orang-outangs were only distantly linked. Classifications of this kind are, however, quite arbitrary. It is possible to arrive at similar inventories by using as terms of comparison the pig, the dog or the mouse : We are bound to find many points in common between them. Similarities between the species are inevitable from an anatomical as well as biological point of view. The reason for this is that the living beings in question all share the same general structure. In the case of animals that breathe, for example, pulmonary alveoli must be present. Nutrition requires a digestive tract and appended glands, and these must of necessity possess a similar structure. The elimination of waste products requires kidneys... There is nothing new or special about any of this. Where we should stop and look more carefully are cases in which there are features present in man that are specific to him alone and that are not to be found in the lineage of the apes.

There is much to be learned from a comparison of the skulls found in the great apes with those of the various human groups mentioned earlier, especially with regard to cranial capacity. In the case of the chimpanzee and the orang-outang, in round figures, the cranial capacity is 400 cc., and 500 cc. or even more in the case of the gorilla. When we come to man, however, the figure gradually rises higher and higher until man reaches his final stage of development. The average figure for man is 1,350 cc., although there are of course variations. The cranial capacity of Neanderthal Man was even slightly greater than this. While the development of the brain kept pace with that of the cranium, it is important to note that the Australopithecus, who made skilful use of the implements he fashioned, possessed a brain that was slightly smaller than that of modern-day gorillas. Man's brain therefore developed first of all in

1. Published by Robert Laffont, Paris, 1978.

terms of quality : The number of neurones increased, and the system of relays and centres grew more and more complex. In this respect, evolution in the apes came to a halt, while man continued to develop until he reached *Homo Sapiens* : The slow evolution of the brain, which was coordinated with the expanding volume of the cranium, was the result of a strict organizational order.

The second extremely important feature concerning the cranium is the occipital foramen magnum. In the apes, the foramen magnum of the occipital bone, through which the brain is connected to the spinal chord, is located in the posterior part of the occipital bone; in man, it is situated in a more anterior position. Thus in the case of man, the centre of gravity of the head coincides more or less with the vertical axis of the cervical column which supports the skull of the individual when in the biped posture, as if the head were balanced on the neck. The foramen itself is almost vertical in the apes, whereas in man it is horizontal.

Other anatomical differences are present, but these are generally less important. Many specialists have, however, drawn attention to the U-shaped form of the mandible (lower jaw), which developed at the same rate as the palate gradually grew longer. There can be no doubt that the first hominids possessed cranial crests, such as the very pronounced crests we see in today's apes—the male gorilla, for example. The dentition is quite different, however : The canines present in the hominids, are not at all the extremely powerful fangs that we find in the male apes. Man's posterior teeth also display a very distinct development.

Let us return to the important question of the long and well-developed upper limbs of the apes and monkeys, for it constitutes a feature of this lineage that is characteristic, even when, as the case of certain species, it serves no functional purpose. The upper limbs, which are in fact the *anterior* limbs in the case of quadruped apes, help to support the animal as it rests on the ground, the weight being distributed on the second phalanges of the second, third, fourth and fifth fingers. With regard to the feet, the weight rests mainly on their outer sides. Almost all apes live in the trees—there are very few exceptions indeed—and the powerful muscles of their upper limbs enable the apes to hang from branches or to swing from one tree to another; these features are in harmony with the functions of the lower limbs which end in prehensile feet (i.e. the big toe is separated from the main body of the foot, like the thumb on the human hand), thus allowing the ape to hold branches in a powerful grasp. These fundamental features of the apes are not present in man.

In contrast, the arched sole of the human foot is perfectly adapted to walking on the three points in contact with the ground : the heel, the joint between the big toe and the first metatarsal (commonly called the ball of the foot), and the joint at the base of the fourth and fifth toes with their corresponding metatarsals. The apes walk and stand on the external side of their feet, and they do not possess the concave form which in man constitutes the arch of the foot.

The vertebral column and pelvis in apes and man present differences due to the biped posture of man. Man possesses a broader pelvis, and his vertebral column displays curves not present in the apes : The dorsal column displays backward convexity, while the entire lumbar and sacral column is marked by forward convexity. In the case of the apes, the entire vertebral column displays a backward convexity. All of these features result from the fact that the upright posture and biped walking pattern are recorded in man's genetic inheritance. As we shall see in the next chapter, however, the biped walking pattern is not an innate feature of human behaviour : A child has to learn how to walk, even though his anatomical structure is already adapted to this specific function.

Biochemical and Genetic Features

As far as its essential characteristics are concerned, each evolved living being is composed of the same kind of tissues. Every handbook of biology describes the general features that are valid for a large number of tissues : Covering tissue, nervous tissue, osseous tissue, muscular tissue, glandular tissue, etc. Each of these possesses a cellular organization with chemical components that are identical from one species to another. The proteins specific to a particular tissue in one animal are very likely to be the same as those in the corresponding tissue of another, even though there is no relation between the two. In the very distant past, a particular gene was responsible for the orientation of a certain cellular function, and this directive remained in the inheritance of the lineage, passing from one descendant to another without any change. Every living being that breathes requires pulmonary alveoli in order to allow the passage of oxygen into the blood and to eliminate carbon dioxide; man requires them just the same as any other animal that breathes. An examination of each and every organic function would reveal that, in order for any animal to survive, its structures must be adapted to its functions. For example, the substances required to sustain life, such as the hemoglobin contained in the red blood cells, result from the specialized functions of certain cells that are controlled by specific genes. Precise chemical characteristics are of necessity shared by all the hemoglobins. They are present in the hemoglobin of man and many other animals, for *there is no alternative.* In his book 'L'Homme en accusation' [*Man Stands Accused*], P.-P. Grassé quotes an extremely judicious comment made by J. de Grouchy on the cellular proteins to be found in both man and chimpanzees : "The manner of utilizing proteinic molecules is probably what accounts for the fact that, in spite of everything, there is a big difference between chimpanzees and man."

Attempts have been made to connect man with the apes by examining their respective genetic inheritance, in particular the number of chromosomes they each possess. The number is not the same : 46 in man, and 48 in the great apes. Since the figures are fairly close to one another, it has been suggested—without a scrap of evidence—that in the case of the apes two chromosomes fused together in order to pass in the case of man from 48 to 46. What counts, however, are the genes. Here we find that one body of opinion holds that the inventory of genes has not been compiled for the apes and is probably very incomplete for man, while another body maintains that "probably less than 2 % of all the genes vary from one species to another" (J. de Grouchy.) Researchers are extremely intrigued by the study of the chromosomes; even today, in spite of the solid discoveries made by paleontology, they are still trying to amalgamate apes and man.

Last but not least, we come to the question of the significance to be attached to the difference in the sexual activity of apes and man, which is linked to the various commands issued by the hormones of each respective species. Leaving aside certain anatomical differences which give rise to minor variations, the main point to be noted is that in man sexual activity is continuous and does not strictly depend on the menstrual cycle of the female. In the apes, the situation is quite different; the menstrual cycle is longer and is marked by a rutting period which is particularly apparent due to the considerable intumescence of the ano-vulvar region, accompanied by a pinkish colouring of the covering skin. These physiological features naturally have a direct influence on the behaviour of apes. Their conduct should been seen in the light of the much more general phenomena that direct animal behaviour.

How Relevant Is the Debate Today?

Since it is hardly possible any longer to defend Darwin's original theory, one might suppose that our better knowledge of man's origins would tend to render somewhat obsolete the controversy surrounding the part played by the simian lineage in our ancestry. Let us make no mistake, however : There are still those who uphold Darwin's theory, and who hunt high and low for arguments to confirm their ideas. These people seem to fall into two categories : The first is composed of a number of paleontologists who make what appear to be extremely flimsy pronouncements; the second is made up of psychologists who are new to the debate.

Among the first, we find paleontologists who begin by noting the discovery of a few teeth, a fragment of mandible or some other meagre fossilized remains, and, once they have given a scientific-sounding name to the individual they have reconstructed largely from their own imagination, they immediately jump to 'solid' conclusions. This is exactly what happened in the case of the Ramapithecus, an ancestor—if that is really what it is—of the pongids, presented by some as a precursor of man. Over the last ten years, importance has also been attributed to the remains of another possible ancestor of the apes, the Dryopithecus. Although there is not the slightest evidence, the Dryopithecus is said to be the form in which the divergence between hominids and apes actually took place.

Specialists in evolution who are used to constructing their theories according to objective observations are particulary incensed by a certain tendency to see in psychology an effective way of solving the problem. P.-P Grassé, in 'L'Homme en accusation' [*Man Stands Accused*], has the following remark to make on this subject :

"There are many psychologists who today see in man nothing more than a chimpanzee, marginally more artful than the other primates. They 'humanize' the apes and 'animalize' man : Anthropomorphism in one case, zoomorphism in the other. According to these psychologists, all human conduct exists in a state that is either dissimulated by appearences, or broadly outlined in the behaviour of the anthropoids. The chimpanzee makes use of implements; he reasons and is capable of conceiving abstract concepts; he possesses a gestural language (pongo-linguistics) that can be perfected through a learning process and which he can use to communicate with man; the chimpanzee also possesses the same sensibility as man, and he is able to express this through painting (Desmond Morris, 1962). This theory has gained widespread popularity among psychologists in Europe and America. A major symposium is planned for Paris at which subjects will be discussed such as the "Self-Awareness and Person-Perception of Experimenters by Chimpanzee Psychologists" (*sic*), a paper to be presented by G. Woodruff of the University of Pennsylvania, U.S.A.; "Use of 'Pongo-linguistics' to determine Mental Representations in the Great Apes : Room for Improvement" (*re-sic*), a paper by R. Fouts of the University of Oklahoma, U.S.A.; and a score of other papers of the same ilk."

In the following chapter, we shall examine the many points on which the behaviour of the two species is in fact quite different.

INNATE AND ACQUIRED BEHAVIOUR :
A COMPARISON BETWEEN MAN
AND THE ANIMALS

The Role of Innate Behaviour
in the Animals

As far as behaviour is concerned, there is a broad gap separating man from the animals. The apes happen to be closer to us than to other species in terms of their anatomy and numerous aspects of their physiology (including the brain functions); it is natural therefore that their behaviour should be the one most frequently compared with our own. Comparative investigation is hampered, however, by the fact that the apes do not possess the power of speech. Furthermore, the experimenter may himself exercise a marked influence on the animals under study, for certain of them display a capacity for observing, memorizing and imitating. Thus it is easy to make animals appear extremely 'intelligent', when in fact all they are doing is expressing themselves through conditioned reflexes, as we shall see in a moment. The apes—and not just the apes—learn much from their contact with man, even if the contact is not particularly recent; this implies that in order to arrive at useful results, the entire past of these animals must be reconstructed. The environment in which the 'zoopsychologist's' examination takes place may also affect the outcome of the tests; the animal should be observed in its natural habitat. The enormous difficulties raised by this kind of study are easy to imagine.

In spite of these drawbacks, however, modern research has been able to distinguish the parts played by the innate and the acquired. We mentioned earlier the innate character of certain animal behaviour; it is worth returning to this subject to highlight even more clearly the contrast with the conduct of man.

There are abundant examples of innate animal behaviour to be found in any handbook of zoology : There is no point in dwelling on the fact. What is of interest, however, is that behavioural patterns may not necessarily be absolutely automatic, owing to a possible adaptation to circumstances. In the case of our friend the 'mutton-bird', the complicated six-month journey could not be performed with such stunning regularity and precision unless the flight programme were adapted to the atmospheric conditions the bird encountered on its way. The duration of the programme and the extremely wide range of external circumstances through which the bird passes make this a truly remarkable example. A much more classic illustration is the case of the nectar-gathering bee which has to identify familiar landmarks in order to find its way back to the nest. It must also indicate to other bees the exact location of pollen and nectar to be gathered. Another example is provided by a certain type of bird which fishes for its food. The bird has to learn how to use its beak, for its first endeavours to peck at the fish miss their target. The reason for this is that in seeing from air to water, the bird has not yet learned to make allowance for the refraction of light rays that occurs between the two. Only after a number of unsuccessful attempts does the bird finally catch the fish. In order to ensure this ultimate success, complex cerebral and medular pathways must first be established.

All of the above phenomena should be examined in the light of our knowledge of the nervous organization that conditions them. At some early stage, nervous 'frameworks' had to be fabricated, as it were, which allowed these complex reactions to take place in response to the stimuli triggering them. The structuring of such a 'framework' is governed by the genetic code; it is the existence, in the D.N.A. tapes of the reproductive cells, of genes which, during embryogeny, dictate that certain cells will differentiate themselves and acquire the functional properties of nervous cells. The genes are transmitted by these same reproductive cells which likewise contain the pre-established programme. The receiving organs must also be sensitive, however, to the stimuli reaching the animal; the latter must be recognized as factors enducing specific responses. These functions all take place within the cells that receive the stimuli : They result from the action of the same complex : D.N.A.–R.N.A. 'messenger'– decoding of the messages–response of the ribosomes and participation of the cytoplasm.

In view of the above, how can we account for the modulations in the animal's responses, or for the adjustment of its innate behaviour according to circumstances? As we know, animals do not have the powers of reasoning or reflection that we find in man. An aeroplane pilot or ship's captain who embarked on the 'mutton-bird's' journey across the Pacific would require navigational instruments; he would have to add the data provided by them to his reading of charts and maps; he would have to plot his course with a ruler, set square, and a pair of compasses. The 'mutton-bird' simply uses its eyes and possibly various other sensory organs and a very small brain in which everything is programmed with a startling degree of miniaturization. If man were to construct a computer to replace the bird's natural attributes, it would have to contain an incredibly complex structure in order to process the same pre-established programme. In this respect, we may perhaps argue that the bird is much more capable than man, owing to its structures. The latter are formed by the proteinic molecules held on the D.N.A. tape that is roughly 1/5,000 millimetre wide and which contains the genetic programme inherited from the bird's progenitors. When the innate behaviour is programmed with such a 'luxurious' complexity, the animal is undoubtedly capable of performances that, without exaggeration, can be described as quite sensational, for man is incapable of similar achievements. As we shall see later on, however, man is endowed with considerable powers of a different kind. Precisely because he has lost his innate behaviour, one of his powers consists in a freedom of action that no animal possesses. This sets him apart from even the most highly organized living beings.

The Capacity for Imitation in Animals and Its Possibly Delayed Effects

We must draw a distinction between true imitation, which consists in the spontaneous reproduction of an action performed by others, and training, which involves a forced apprenticeship in a behaviour that the animal is subsequently to repeat.

Spontaneous imitation is a feature characteristic of the apes, and man makes use of it for training purposes. Left to themselves, apes appear to enjoy mimicking what they see : Chimpanzees are past masters in the art of imitation. They seem to derive pleasure from it, especially if the action they are imitating provides them with a certain degree of satisfaction. It has been said that chimpanzees do not behave consistently, but they are perhaps able to attach a certain significance to the action imitated if, at the end of the imitation, they receive some kind of reward. Over and over again, we read reports of how chimpanzees have watched humans open a cupboard containing titbits and have repeated the exact same movements in order to obtain the desired food. Imitations can be performed after only a short period of time, as well as after a more or less long period; they may also be repeated, especially if the chimpanzee experiences a certain satisfaction in his mimicry.

Chimpanzees are also able to imitate human movements that have remained in their memory, even after a certain time has elapsed, and even though these movements may not have the slightest significance for them. In one of his works, P.-P. Grassé relates the following anecdote : In Africa, one of his chimpanzees on several occasions watched a worker use a machete to cut grass and dig holes in the ground. When transported to an island to undergo observation in its natural habitat, and thus left to itself, the chimpanzee seized an implement of this kind left lying there and began to cut the grass and attempt to dig a hole in the ground, just as it had seen the worker use the same tool for the same purpose at least ten days earlier!

As for training, we are all familiar with its many spectacular forms, from the acts performed at the circus; it is not limited, however, to the most highly evolved animals on the scale of mammals. The apes are joined by such animals as bears, elephants, dolphins, dogs, etc., all of which might at first sight suggest the existence of types of intelligence which tend too quickly to be assimilated with human intelligence. It is difficult not to be astounded by the various actions that dolphins are able to perform; they have even been trained to act as auxiliaries in the execution of naval operations. There is every indication that the performance of the dolphins can be very sophisticated indeed.

Only when we read about them in such eminently serious studies as P.-P. Grassé's 'L'Homme en accusation' [Man Stands Accused], can we credit the amazing performances of dogs, for they have been scientifically investigated.

At the Laboratoire d'Evolution des Êtres Organisés [Laboratory for the Study of Evolution in Organized Living Beings], an Italian dog-trainer presented the performances of a female poodle, named Dana, who not only knew the figures 0 to 9, the signs + and =, but also the twenty-five letters of the Italian alphabet. Dana was perfectly able to recognize the twenty-five letters and arrange them in such an order that a very brief and simple Italian phrase appeared. Obviously, Dana's cerebral structures and functions did not permit her to understand what she was actually doing, but she nevertheless possessed an extraordinary ability to memorize, which enabled her to distinguish between so many figurative signs; she obeyed a series of conditioned reflexes ordering her to arrange the letters in the desired order.

Thus, the dog-trainer commanded Dana to fetch and arrange on the ground the figure 3, the sign +, the figure 4, and the sign =. Having carried out these four orders, Dana of her own accord fetched and added to the sum the figure 7. This final action was executed without any command being issued, as far as the laboratory observers could detect.

Nobody is suggesting that the poodle was able to read and count : Her brain would not enable her to do either. Dana was simply following orders received from her trainer. Had anyone else given the commands, Dana would not have reacted. In P.-P. Grassé's opinion : "It is certain that Dana recognized a fairly large number of words when spoken, and replied by a posture, or a series of barks that were always the same... The wish to receive a lump of sugar or a biscuit generally motivated the animal's actions... With its relatively small brain, the dog was able to perform astoundingly complex tricks, which for the public would mean that Dana was highly intelligent. As far as I am concerned, however, all I could find was the result of conditioned reflexes to the exclusion of the awareness of the situation."

If the tight bond that exists between the animal and its trainer is broken, the experiment is doomed to failure. In contrast to this, my grandson's knowledge of figures is roughly equal to Dana's, and he is able to count up to ten : Providing he is well-disposed toward the person who asks him, he will give an exact reply to *anyone* who gives him figures to add. At a stage where the child must count with his fingers, he will make more or less overt use of this trick which has been taught to him. His reply will therefore be the result of intelligence and will be based on reflection; it will be given in the absence of the parents who taught him the fundamental principles of simple reasoning, and as a consequence, the problem may be solved in *any circumstances whatsoever* (except for the occasional childish fit of obstinacy.)

The considerable development of certain capacities for imitation and memorization may, however, lead to behaviour among apes that could appear to be acquired. Young chimpanzees are able to identify poisonous fruits in the forest, once they have been taught by their mother to recognize them. This useful aspect of the chimpanzee's behaviour in its natural environment is quite different from another–this time innate–feature of its conduct which is often stressed : This is the chimpanzee's innate ability to build a night shelter in the trees, even in cases where the chimpanzee in question has never experienced life in the forest before. In contrast to this, certain apes in Gabon seem to obey an imitative tradition in washing manioc tubers. Perhaps their ancestors watched humans washing the tubers at some point after manioc was first introduced into Africa in the seventeenth century. Nevertheless, the role of the parents in the education of the young ape remains not only effective, but beyond dispute : The young apes imitate their parents, but that is as far as their intellectual capacity goes.

It is a shame that totally false notions are so often spread concerning the intelligence and reasoning faculties that certain animals supposedly possess. The public impact of these mistaken ideas is very great indeed when they are put forward by important authorities and supported by the sort of pictures one is likely to see in the course of a major television programme. Such was the case during a recent broadcast, in which an underwater explorer provided a commentary on a sequence of film intended to illustrate these very qualities in animals. According to the commentator, the sequence demonstrated that the octopus was endowed with a capacity for reasoning. In fact, however, the mollusc in question displays a nervous system—composed of a few meagre ganglions and two nerves—that is about as rudimentary as that of the annulated worm. In common with all the molluscs, the octopus does not possess a brain; its behaviour is automatic, for it is guided by various tropisms. If we ascribe to the octopus powers that it cannot have, we are in fact overlooking its anatomy and physiology : It does not contain any more powers than the mussel. It is as if we decided to study the properties of the bile in an animal that has no liver to produce it. In this particular case, the experimenter took for a deliberate action what was in fact nothing but the purely accidental result of an automatic impulse in one of the tentacles of the octopus. In spite of this, millions of television viewers, unaware of the real situation, must have been convinced that the experiment indeed demonstrated a certain level of intelligence in the animal. The fact is, however, that the octopus does not possess the nervous organization which is required for the expression of any form of reflection.

Animals Rarely Use Implements

Apes are not the only animals to use tools. Less evolved species sometimes use implements for precise purposes—gathering food in particular. In this context, ornithologists have discovered the existence of astonishing behavioural patterns which are specific to certain species, as follows :

– A species of chaffinch native to the Pacific possesses a beak that does not permit it to catch certain preys. The chaffinch therefore grasps a thorn in its beak and uses it to poke at the ground and the roots of trees in order to force insects out. Once these have emerged, the bird has no trouble in snapping them up.

– In Africa, there is a species of vulture that possesses a curiously cunning skill : It consists in breaking the extremely resistant shells of ostrich eggs. To do this, the vulture picks up fairly heavy stones (roughly 140 g.) in its beak, and drops them from a certain height onto the egg. Once the egg is broken by the impact of the stone, the vulture descends to devour its contents.

The origins of this use of implements by birds is unknown. It would seem, moreover, to be an extremely rare phenomenon.

While the great apes that live in the forest are able to use branches to strike an attacker, they also have many other *capacities for using implements.* I can well remember the stories told to me long ago at Yale University in the United States by specialists in ape behaviour and their collaborators at J. F. Fulton's laboratory devoted to this purpose. The sometimes successful attempts of the apes to escape their cage by using whatever tools lay to hand, and their endeavours to rid themselves of the electrodes implanted in their brain, indicated definite skills on the part of the chimpanzees or macaques in question. There are plenty of examples to support the idea behind the expression 'as artful as a cartload of monkeys', although we should beware of taking the phrase too literally, for it has its limits.

Goodall has noted that chimpanzees sometimes use a twig to capture termites. They push the twig into the termitary and wait for the termites automatically to accumulate on the twig. This action would appear to be full of cunning ingenuity. P.-P. Grassé nevertheless expresses doubts as to this 'invention' of the apes : In many regions of Africa, he has noted that the natives, who regard soldier termites as something of a delicacy, use the same procedure to attract the insects. P.-P. Grassé wonders whether the chimpanzees happened, at some point, to see humans in the process of capturing termites with a twig and simply imitated them. He himself observed a chimpanzee capturing termites in this way in the Ivory Coast. Others may perhaps go so far as to speculate that it was in fact man who imitated the chimpanzees.

Whatever the case, one fact is sure concerning the animal's use of implements, and it is of fundamental importance : *No example exists of the spontaneous and deliberate fabrication of an imple-*

ment by an animal. The great apes, which in terms of nervous organization are the most evolved of the animals, are intellectually incapable of realizing that it is possible to use one implement to fashion another destined to serve a specific purpose. The logical connection between the two actions is totally beyond them.

Let us remember that millions of years ago, the most primitive hominid, the Australopithecus, was capable of performing the two operations, one after the other : The point is proved by the existence of tools whose cutting edge was produced with the help of another implement. This constitutes a characteristic feature dividing the great apes from the representatives of the first wave of hominids at present known.

The Loss of Man's Innate Behaviour

Man has almost completely lost his innate behaviour, but that does not mean that he is born without it : In his heredity, which is recorded in the genetic code, there is a wide variety of *potentialities connected to his structures,* all of which are ready to ensure many different functions and to play their part once man decides that the time has come. Through the loss of numerous instinctive complexes, man has gained his freedom.

At birth, man still possesses the innate behavioural pattern which consists in sucking; a pattern that is vital for the nourishment of the newborn infant. Although by nature a biped, man still has to learn how to walk in the posture to which his structures are adapted. In contrast to this, however, his conduct is in no way determined by any of his genes, a point on which he differs from the animals, whose behaviour is innate and whose conduct is only influenced by factors connected with circumstances. In this context, the phenomena of imitation (mentioned above) and their accompanying consequences might perhaps be confused, in the case of the animals, with what seem essentially to be acquired behavioural patterns, but in fact are not. On the other hand, it is not possible to generalize or to take the exception as the rule. Indeed, the origins of exceptions–such as the extremely rare examples of the use of implements–have not at all been explained and therefore remain shrouded in mystery. The point here is to establish a general principle on a wide variety of facts; for if we insist on the exceptions and ignore the majority of cases, we are bound to draw the wrong conclusions.

We can state for certain that innate behaviour in man has almost disappeared. At birth, our genetic code provides us, not with automatic behavioural patterns, but rather with general capabilities : It is up to man to ensure that these capabilities are 'brought to fruition', as it were.

Everyone is born with nervous centres in which stimuli are received, analysed, interpreted and transformed into a wide range of responses. Apart from cases of identical twins, who are formed from a single fertilized ovum, everyone is different from a structural point of view. This implies *ipso facto* that nobody has exactly the same capabilities. This inequality is linked to our constitution. Within a single family, where the inherited chromosomes are the same, there will always be differences between the offspring. Side by side with obvious physical resemblances, vast differences in intellectual ability may exist–although there may be major physical differences as well. The latter is always a possibility, even though in certain families dominant features may be noted in several generations.

Man's Mental Faculties Highlighted
By Social Intercourse

In this respect, no two people's capabilities are the same. Their faculties depend first and foremost on their structures. The genes govern the development of the brain and exercise a constant influence on the biology of the cells and the functions of the associative neurones. Their number is so great that we do not know to which power we should multiply the billions of neurones in order to arrive at an exact figure [1]. Each brain cell differentiated itself from cellular substances that have not yet acquired specialized functions at the embryonic stage, but each cell contains the entire code that is to govern the subsequent course of evolution. It possesses its D.N.A., on which the genes are held, and all the other substances required for the transmission of messages, on which depends the quality of the particular function provided; this may vary from one individual to another with regard to certain relays and nervous centres.

Certain families exist that are particularly well-endowed with individuals who, for one reason or another, display talents that single them out from among their contemporaries, often themselves

1. A recent estimate suggested a figure roughly equal to 1 followed by fifty-nine zeros! (J. Hamburger).

extremely competent in their field. There are also people who may be classed as 'exceptionally gifted'; either they are child prodigies or they are people whose abilities are way above average. This type of superiority is not necessarily present, however, in all the members of a same family.

A considerable influence is exerted on the young by their family and those surrounding them. One may indeed ask, in general terms, just what would become of us if we did not live in society. For it is indeed social intercourse, in its widest possible sense, which, through education, upbringing and the transfer of knowledge, enables us to make use of our abilities. In the case of the animals, most of the information they use comes from their individual inheritance. They do not possess the wide powers of adaptation that man enjoys owing to the loss of the innate behaviour controlled by the genes. By and large, the animals follow patterns of conduct that are rigidly set.

P.-P. Grassé has defined the role played by social intercourse in the following terms : "An evolution that was purely biological would not in itself have been sufficient to shape man; the assistance of life in society was needed, with its accumulation of knowledge beyond the genetic code, in order for the human spirit to be freed of all instinctive automatism."

For life in society to play a part, however, communication was necessary. The most ancient and most direct form of this is articulate speech, which is a phenomenon that exists only in man. It first requires a thought, and then, it needs words to express that thought. In the case of deaf-mutes, the two are separated, for while such people are able to think, they are not able to express themselves in speech.

As for the animals, the sounds emitted by parrots and other birds are mere acts of imitation, and therefore do not pose any problems. Other animals do indeed communicate, however, exchanging information by acoustic processes : They employ sounds that are audible to the human ear or inaudible (ultrasonic sounds), as the case may be. They also communicate by visual and even olfactory (chemical) signals, all of which are governed by the animals' automatic behavioural patterns. Higher mammals are able to convey messages to each other, thus transmitting their understanding of a particular situation : They undoubtedly emit inarticulate sounds. These have been recorded in the animals' natural surroundings, and it has thus been possible to distinguish vocalizations whose variety and abundance are not at all in keeping with the animals' psychic powers. Thus the gibbons and cercopithecoid monkeys, although psychically less evolved than the gorillas and chimpanzees, nevertheless display a much wider vocal repertory. All the same, there does not seem to be much real dialogue between individual apes or monkeys.

In the United States, psychologists have tried–in their own way–to coax the great apes to speak, and they claim to have succeeded. As in the case of Dana the performing poodle mentioned above, however, this is primarily a matter of training. R.A. and B.T. Gardner were able to teach a chimpanzee eighty-five signs in the deaf-mute code : The test-chimpanzee was able to use three or four signs at a time to express its wishes. Another trainer used different symbols with another animal. The outcome of all these tests was in fact very much the same as the results obtained with Dana : The animal learned the letters and figures taught to it in advance by the trainer in countless question-and-answer sessions. When the time came to perform, the animal merely appears to have repeated what it had learned.

In contrast, true language results from a highly sophisticated intellectual process. It not only transmits an image, but *acts as a vehicle for abstract ideas.* Through language, we are able to convey these ideas, and express our sentiments. For man, language is an infinitely precious acquisition which is unique to his species.

THE INFLUENCE OF CREATIVE EVOLUTION
IN MAN'S DEVELOPMENT

Since the beginning of the twentieth century, great progress has been made in research into the origins and evolution of man, due to contributions supplied by many different disciplines. Ultra-microscopic and biochemical studies of the cell would seem recently to have brought the most light to bear on the factors governing the course of events. Far be it from me, however, to minimalize the contributions of the natural sciences, zoology in particular, or paleontology, which are the fundamental underpinnings of any investigation in this field, for it is these, and related disciplines, that are responsible for our knowledge of the ordered course of evolution.

Today, we know that the first wave of humans appeared on earth some five million years ago (six million years ago for certain researchers, and less for others). The waves that were to follow have also been more or less precisely located in time. What gaps still remain, however, in our knowledge due to the rarity of fossils! What large quantities of statements have appeared concerning the supposed relationship between human groups and the lineage that produced the apes (which is placed next to the human lineage on the genealogical table), none of which is supported by any valid argument! What else are they but simple hypotheses designed to square with certain researchers' preconceived ideas?

The very small quantity of paleolontological specimens documenting the origins of mankind should make us proceed with extreme caution. There can be no doubt that many fossils exist which have not yet been discovered; some of them never will be. Chronological data bearing on apes and humans alike may one day be modified by future discoveries. Whatever happens, however, there are solid arguments to reject the theory that man is descended from the apes.

Even if it becomes possible to trace the human lineage much further back in time than the oldest human forms at present thought to be known, we shall never arrive at the idea that man was born of simian forms, whose descendants are today's great apes.

While discoveries made over the last few decades have gradually pushed back the appearance of the first human forms to more and more distant periods (from hundreds of thousands to millions of years), the basic problem remains the same. Whatever the answer, the discoveries do not indicate that man is descended from a fully developed lineage of apes.

What *is* new is our knowledge of the activity that takes place within the cell and the information every human cell contains which is recorded in the genes. These are held on the helix-shaped D.N.A. tape which is over one metre long. When compared with the dimensions of the cell itself, which are measured in units of $1/1,000$ millimetre, the length of the tape is colossal. In the case of primitive life forms, such as bacteria, the essential characteristics of the species, which govern its functions and reproduction, are recorded on the same D.N.A. tape, except that for the bacteria, the tape is roughly a million times shorter. The general concept of evolution can only be explained in terms of this difference. Whatever ideas we may entertain on the factors that have determined the course of evolution, the basic fact remains the same. The anatomical features and the functions of the living beings to come later on, which will differ from species to species, will all be dependent on the genetic code governing their appearance, maintenance and possible modifications.

We have already noted how some scientists, although constantly preoccupied with the need to push back the frontiers of knowledge, stop short at the very question they themselves have raised : What is the origin of the genetic code? J. Monod seems to have been content to dispense with the 'problem' by simply stating that 'it is an enigma'. In fact however, this is only the first of our problems, one which science seems incapable of answering. A second enigma exists and that is the factor determining the *increase of information over the course of time* in the genetic code, a phenomenon that is strikingly evident. Scientists are currently trying to discover why an original plan was devised *which was subsequently enriched to a considerable degree* over the course of hundreds, if not thousands of millions of years.

It is easier to understand the capacity of the genetic code for giving orders when we take into consideration the part the code plays in the formation of the individual, a process that is more readily accessible to us. As we all know, our genes are inherited from our father and mother. After the spermatozoon has united with the ovule, our genetic inheritance is initially contained in a single cell. A series of cellular divisions then takes place which transmits this same inheritance to all the cells thus formed. The genes held on the D.N.A. tape govern the differenciation of the cells within the embryo, which, after a series of extremely complex transformations, result in tissues and organs that each have very specific functions. In normal individuals, all these different features function together in perfect harmony.

Let us take, for example, two human characteristics that have not always been the same in the various human types : These are (as we have seen) the size and development of the brain. The size of the brain depends on the capacity for growth of the body as a whole, according to various influences. The genetic inheritance of the Australopithecus cannot in this respect have been the same as that of man, because certain fossils of the Australopithecus indicate a body height of 1.25 to 1.50 metres, while modern man is some 40 centimetres taller. The factors influencing size are very diverse : A large number of genes cannot fail to play a role (in spite of the possible existence of genes that fulfil multiple functions). New information must of necessity have been added to modern man in comparison with the Australopithecus. It may be conditioned by new genes that are active, or indeed by the appearance of new genes which perhaps inhibit the activities of pre-existing genes. The same applies to the many factors governing the development of the brain : This latter process must have been coordinated with a large number of modifications, including that of the cranial capacity, for we know that the cranial capacity of the Australopithecus was roughly one third of that of present-day man.

The action of the genes does not, however, explain everything concerning man and his evolution. As we have mentioned above, the genetic inheritance governs the attribution of various capacities which man uses with greater or lesser effectiveness. While the latter certainly depends on the quality of these capacities, man's personal wish to use his natural gifts also plays a part, for man has the feedom to choose. The animals bear the burden of innate conduct and are unable to escape from a host of behavioural patterns dictated by their genetic inheritance. In this respect, comparative studies of human and animal behaviour have provided us with extremely important data. Furthermore, man possesses characteristics and qualities which he owes to the society in which he lives and from which he draws a fund of knowledge accumulated over generations.

It is up to each individual to make the personal effort required to increase this intellectual capital, so that, in their turn, those who come after him may reap the benefits of this new knowledge.

The appearance of new attributes in man does not simply owe its origin to the genes and the increase of information which has progressively been added to our inheritance. These facts allow us to join P.-P. Grassé in stating that : "To a certain extent, man influenced his own development by contributing to the enrichment of his inherited assets; without this active participation in his own evolution, man would not be what he is today. This form of evolution, which is unique within the animal kingdom, radically separates man from the animals. "

III

THE FIRST ANSWER OF THE HOLY SCRIPTURES : THE BIBLE

THE NEED TO KNOW THE ORIGIN
AND HISTORY OF THE TEXTS

Owing to the narratives of the Creation to be found in the Old Testament, the Bible represents the first Scripture of a monotheistic religion ever to provide data concerning the origins of man. Not until the advent of the age of science, in which the question is viewed in the light of material facts, has the subject been approached in the West from any angle other than that of various philosophies or considerations based on the teachings of the Bible. For many centuries, the latter were held to come from God Himself, for the Bible was regarded as the Word of God. There could be absolutely no question, therefore, of disputing a single statement it contained.

If today we still preserved the same general approach toward the Bible, the contrast between scientific data and the ideas on the subject set forth in the Book of Genesis would not only be glaringly obvious, but also insurmountable. Those who still uphold this classic approach to the narratives of the Creation contained in the Old Testament would not be able to accept the idea of evolution : They would be extremely incensed as far as man was concerned, and they would not tolerate for the rest of the animal kingdom any concept other than the traditional notion of the fixity of species as laid down in the Bible.

It is not so long ago that any comparison between an opinion expressed in the Bible and secular data of any kind was violently rejected as a potential danger to religious belief. Criticism of a statement contained in the Bible invariably led to scandal, for it implied that certain assertions were wrong. Even today, I have often noticed the considerable embarrassment of educated Christians when confronted with certain questions on this subject.

Let us immediately mention one problem which perfectly illustrates the uneasiness certain assertions can cause :

Earlier in the present work, we stated that the average lifespan of a human generation was twenty-five years, constituting four generations per century. This is the average figure which can be deduced from genealogical tables when established over several centuries. Assuming the Australopithecus was the first representative of the hominids, that he appeared roughly five million years ago and that he disappeared at the earliest two million years ago, we must conclude that 80,000 to 200,000 generations separate us from our first ancestor (although the figure may indeed be higher.) What can we say, therefore, of the genealogy that appears in the Gospel According to Luke (3, 23-38) which traces the ancestors of Jesus back to Adam, and from which it would appear that seventy-six generations of humans preceded Jesus?

A number of answers have been put forward to explain this, and they vary considerably. Many people simply ignore Luke's text, while others reply that the text has been mistranslated, claiming that the phrase 'son of...', repeated in Luke's text, perhaps means for certain of the lineage, that two names which thus follow one another may not, however, refer to two succeeding generations... There are very few commentators who think that in view of the circumstances in which this Gospel was written, and in particular the sources at Luke's disposal, the text ought not to be taken literally, any more than other passages in the Gospels. In the light of our present knowledge of the history of the texts, however, this explanation seems to be the most in keeping with reality. Any reply that evades this obvious difficulty is illogical and might raise doubts as to the authenticity of the entire text, in the case of those who are unable to accept totally irrational explanations.

We are not mistreating the Gospels when we point out the existence of passages that can no longer be accepted in the twentieth century because they contain statements that have been proven wrong. On the contrary, we are in fact doing them a service by highlighting the factors that led the Biblical authors to write inaccurate information. In so doing, we are rendering more plausible the existence and mission of Jesus Christ. A genealogy of Jesus that reaches back to Adam by way of Joseph is, moreover, totally illogical, for Joseph had absolutely nothing to do with the arrival of Jesus in the world. What Luke's Gospel in fact gives us is the supposed genealogy of Joseph, whereas the only logical genealogy for Jesus would obviously be that of Mary.

This extended example clearly illustrates the illogicalities to which a *stricto sensu* interpretation of certain Biblical texts can lead. It indicates the need to possess detailed knowledge of the origin and history of the texts, in order to understand the reasons why we must today read the Bible differently from the way we have read it until fairly recently. Unless we are aware of certain facts concerning the texts, we shall not be able to proceed to a commentary of particular passages, nor shall we learn the lessons that must be drawn from them.

MODERN APPROACHES
TO THE BOOKS OF THE BIBLE

The Old Testament

The Old Testament has many authors, and the history of the texts is as confused as it is unknown. In my previous work, *The Bible, the Qur'an and Science,* I provided extracts on this aspect of the Bible taken from works written by members of the clergy. In particular, I turned to the modern edition of the Bible, translated into French under the supervision of the Biblical School of Jerusalem [1] and published in separate volumes.

Originally, there were several texts and not just one. In the first century B.C., there was a tendency toward the establishment of a single text, but it was not until a century after Christ that the Biblical text was definitively established. The most ancient Hebrew version of the Biblical text probably dates from the ninth century A.D. The Septuagint was most likely the first translation in Greek. It dates from the third century B.C. and was written by Jews in Alexandria. It was on this text that the New Testament was based. It remained authoritative until the seventh century A.D. The basic Greek texts in general use in the Christian world are from the manuscripts catalogued under the title *Codex Vaticanus* in the Vatican City and *Codex Sinaiticus* at the British Museum in London. They both date from the fourth century A.D.

All of these versions have enabled specialists to piece together so-called 'middle-of-the-road' texts, a sort of compromise between the different versions. The same process is still carried on today : The 'Traduction Œcuménique de l'Ancien Testament' *[The Ecumenical Translation of the Old Testament]* [2] is a work of synthesis compiled

1. Published by Editions du Cerf, Paris, 1972.
2. Published by Editions du Cerf et les Bergers et les Mages, Paris, 1975.

by over one hundred Catholic and Protestant specialists. The aim of this edition is to establish a text that is acceptable to Churches which do not always share identical ideas on certain meanings and commentaries.

The Old Testament is a collection of works of greatly differing length and many different genres. The works were written in several languages over a period of more than nine hundred years, and they were based on oral traditions. Many of them were corrected and completed in accordance with events or special requirements, often at periods that were very distant from one another. The first texts probably appeared at the beginning of the Israelite monarchy, around the eleventh century B.C. It was at this period that a body of scribes was formed among the members of the royal household. These early texts constitute fragments scattered here and there throughout the various collections of the Old Testament.

It was not until slightly later–in the tenth century B.C. according to some, in the ninth century B.C. according to others–that the so-called 'Yahvist' text appeared, in which we find the first five books of the Bible, known as the 'Pentateuch'. The text derives its name from the fact that in it God is called 'Yahveh.' [1] Later, the so-called 'Elohist' text was added, for in this text God is known as 'Elohim', and in the sixth century B.C. the 'Sacerdotal' version appeared, named after the priests of the Temple at Jerusalem who composed it; this version was also added to the previous two texts.

The Pentateuch is of particular interest to our present study because it contains the Book of Genesis. Here we find not just one, but two narratives of the creation of the world and of man : The most recent narrative is taken from the Sacerdotal version, and it is this narrative which figures at the beginning of today's Bibles. The earlier text, the Yahvist version, comes after the Sacerdotal version and is extremely short. Most people think–wrongly–that there is only one narrative of the Creation on the Old Testament. The two different origins of the narratives are fully acknowledged by Christian exegetes, most notably Father de Vaux, who was at one time Head of the Biblical School of Jerusalem. In his commentaries on the Book of Genesis, Father de Vaux clearly indicates the sections of text which belong to each respective version. The ancient idea that Moses himself was the author of the Book of Genesis is, of course,

---

1. We must note, however, that, in the Yahvist narrative of the Creation given by the English Revised Standard Version of the Bible, God is not named 'Yahveh' but 'The Lord God', as we shall see in the next chapter.

unacceptable. Nobody knows who actually wrote the Yahvist and Elohist versions.

The numerous books of prophecy cover the period reaching from the eighth to the second centuries B.C. The first of these were the Book of Elias and the Book of Elisha.

The historical books provide an account of the entire history of the Jewish people from their entry into the Promised Land–which probably took place toward the end of the thirteenth century B.C.–to the second century B.C. While the events of the second century B.C. may seem to be correctly related, in many books dealing with other periods historical accuracy has by no means been respected : Religious and moral considerations outweigh any fidelity to history, such as we understand it today.

The final category is reserved for the books of poetry and wisdom, such as the Psalms, which were composed by several different authors : David, as well as various priests and levites. The authors of many books remain unknown.

We may therefore state that the Bible is composed of books whose contents are extremely disparate. The texts have undergone considerable rewriting in the course of time, especially with regard to the subject at hand. Christianity received the heritage of the Old Testament, to which the authors of the Gospels adhered very strictly. We should note, however, that during the first centuries of Christianity, a very stringent selection was made of texts relating to Jesus. This was not the case for the Old Testament, which was more or less accepted in its entirety.

The first five books, among which we find Genesis, constitute what is called by the Jews the Torah or Law; they relate the events that took place from the origin of the world to the death of Moses. It is perhaps the questions raised by these books that have caused the most embarrassment; for centuries, there was absolutely no discussion either of the text or of the idea that it should be attributed to Moses.

How could the situation have been otherwise? There are passages in the books themselves which indicate that Moses wrote particular narratives or laws. Moreover, God Himself commanded Moses to describe a certain event in the book of Exodus. Philo of Alexandria, a secular author writing at the time of Jesus, supported this theory. In the first century B.C., Flavius Josephus seconded it. Above all, the Gospels themselves (John 5, 46-47) tell us that Jesus himself bore witness to the origin of these narratives.

In his 'Introduction Générale au Pentateuque' [*General Introduction to the Pentateuch*], Father de Vaux has provided an extremely detailed historical study of the criticism the text has raised from this point of view. I have outlined it in 'La Bible, le Coran et la Science' [*The Bible, the Qur'an and Science*]. Apart from the objections raised in the twelfth century by Abenezra, traditional ideas concerning the origins of the Pentateuch were never questioned. In the sixteenth century, a protestant named Carlstadt noted that Moses could not have written the account of his own death which appears in Deuteronomy (34,5-12), even though, as Carlstadt adds, it is written in the same style as the rest of the book. Father de Vaux goes on to cite other critical works which refuse to attribute to Moses at least part of the Pentateuch. Prominent among these is the 'Histoire critique du Vieux Testament' [*Critical History of the Old Testament*] (1678), by Richard Simon, a father at the Oratory. In it, Simon emphasized the chronological difficulties, the repetitions, the confusion of stories and stylistic differences in the Pentateuch. The book caused a scandal, and Simon was dismissed from his order. His theory was not followed, and Moses continued to be considered the author of the Pentateuch. In history books published at the beginning of the eighteenth century, we thus find references to antiquity which very often proceed from what 'Moses had written.' It was obviously very difficult to contradict a theory strengthened by Jesus Himself in the Gospels (John, Matthew, Luke) and the New Testament (Acts of the Apostles, Letters of Paul), as cited by Father de Vaux.

Jean Astruc, the physician of King Louis XV, reopened the debate in 1753 by publishing his 'Conjectures sur les Mémoires originaux dont il paraît que Moyse s'est servi pour composer le livre de la Genèse' [*Conjectures on the original writings which it appears Moses used to compose the Book of Genesis*]. He pointed out that two texts, each distinguished by the way in which God was either called Yahveh or Elohim, were present side by side in Genesis : The latter quite obviously contained two juxtaposed texts.

Father de Vaux cites other, more recent commentators who are inclined to divide the Pentateuch into four main texts :
— The Yahvist text, dating from the ninth century B.C.;
— the Elohist text, slightly more recent;
— Deuteronomy, which for some dates from the eighth century B.C. and for others from the seventh century B.C. (Father de Vaux);
— the Sacerdotal text, which dates from during or after the exile in Babylon (sixth century B.C.)

Commentators have, however, distinguished various sources in each of the texts. Nine of them exist in the Sacerdotal text, which contains one of the two accounts of the Creation, not including the additions spread out among eight different authors" (Father de

Vaux.) Thus the Pentateuch is shown to be formed from numerous traditions brought together by 'editors' who either juxtaposed their compilations or adapted the stories for the sake of harmonization.

Modern Christian exegetes of the Old Testament note that this multiplicity of sources remains perfectly compatible with the general concept of the *inspired* nature of the books of the Bible. In the chapter entitled 'La Révélation de la Vérité, La Bible et les Evangiles' [*The Revelation of the Truth, The Bible and the Gospels*] which appears in Jean Guitton's work 'Mon petit catéchisme'[*My Little Catechism*] [1], we read that "God did not write these books Himself, instead He had them written by breathing into the apostles and prophets *the things He wanted us to know.* This breath is called 'inspiration'. The books written by the prophets are called 'divinely inspired books'."

These authors all wrote their works at different periods and according to the manners and customs of their day. We therefore find various 'literary genres' scattered throughout the Bible. This notion has gained general acceptance so that we are not surprised, on reading either the Old Testament or the Gospels, to find divinely inspired subjects side by side with affirmations derived from certain secular beliefs carried over from traditions whose origins are often obscure.

This approach to the books of the Bible, which takes account of modern data on the texts, is very different from the position held by commentators until fairly recent times : In days gone by, it was not possible to acknowledge the possiblility of such a preponderantly human role in the written compilation of what were originally oral traditions.

Today, it is easy to explain the existence of historical inaccuracies, implausible statements or blatant contradictions : They should no longer cause any embarrassment, even though we are fully aware of the incompatibility that is to be found between secular knowledge and certain statements in the Old Testament, bearing on the subject of the present work as well as other topics.

The Second Vatican Council (1962-1965) clearly acknowledged the imperfections and obsolescence of certain texts in the Bible, as reflected in the Conciliar Document N° 4 on the Revelation [2]. The following two sentences define the position of the Catholic Church on the overall worth of the text, as well as the impossibility of taking literally certain passages :

1. Published by Desclée de Brouwer, Paris, 1978.
2. Published by Le Centurion, Paris, 1966.

"In view of the human situation prevailing before Christ's foundation of salvation, the Books of the Old Testament enable everybody to know who is God and who is man, and also the way in which God, in his justice and mercy, behaves toward men. These books, *even though they contain material which is imperfect and obsolete,* nevertheless bear witness to truly divine teachings."

The New Testament

The only passages from the Gospels to which we shall later refer are mainly extracts taken from the Gospel According to Luke. They are essentially a rewriting of Old Testament material with a few adjustments. Christian researchers have themselves discovered in the composition of the Gospels such a complex variety of sources that—as for the Old Testament—we must once again be aware of the circumstances present at the time the texts were written, in order to gain a more accurate idea of the reality of the situation.

It is a great shame that until very recently, the Gospel writers have always been presented as eye-witnesses to the facts they relate. Commentators have provided such a wealth of detail on these authors—their professions, for example—that we should apparently be in no doubt as to their status as direct witnesses. In fact they were nothing of the sort. As Cardinal Daniélou has shown in his studies of the early days of Christianity, doctrinal rivalries found their expression in the different ways events were related.

Each writer seems to have approached the facts in the light of his own opinions and adapted the texts accordingly. Matthew, Mark, Luke and John, who composed their texts between 70 A.D. and 110 A.D., provide narratives that are often quite different. Paul wrote his Letters many years before them. According to modern exegetes, not a single one of the authors of the New Testament actually witnessed the events he describes. The Gospel writings did not become known until relatively late. In the introduction to the 'Traduction Œcuménique de la Bible, Nouveau Testament' [*Ecumenical Translation of the Bible, New Testament*] which appeared in 1972, we read the following : "Before 140 A.D., there was, in any case, no account by which one might have recognized a collection of evangelical writings."

O. Culmann, in his book 'Le Nouveau Testament' [*The New Testament*] [1], notes that the evangelists were only the "spokesmen of

1. Published by Presses Universitaires de France, Paris, 1967.

the early Christian community who wrote down the oral tradition. For thirty or forty years, the Gospels had existed as an almost exclusively oral tradition : The latter only transmitted sayings and isolated narratives. The evangelists brought them together, each in his own way, according to his own character and theological preoccupations. They linked the narrations and sayings handed down by the prevailing tradition... It must be noted that the needs of preaching, worship and teaching, more than biographical consider-ations, were what guided the early community in writing down the tradition of the life of Jesus. By describing the events of Christ's life, the apostles illustrated the truth of the faith they were preaching. Their sermons are what caused the descriptions to be recorded in writing ".

This is exactly how the commentators of the 'Traduction Œcu-ménique de la Bible' [*Ecumenical Translation of the Bible*] describe the writing of the Gospels : "The evangelists... have collected and recorded in writing the material given to them by the oral tradition. " The Gospel According to John does not contain nearly so many episodes in common with the other three. The Gospels According to Matthew, Mark and Luke are–highly euphemistically–called 'syn-optic' Gospels, because Luke, and to a lesser degree Matthew, contain a number of very important verses which do not appear in any of the other three texts [1].

In their book 'Synopse des quatre Evangiles' [*Synopsis of the Four Gospels*] [2], Fathers Benoit and Boismard, both professors at the Biblical School of Jerusalem, stress the evolution of the text in stages parallel to the evolution of the tradition. In an extremely helpful diagram, reproduced in 'La Bible, le Coran et la Science' [*The Bible, the Qu'ran and Science*], they explain how the final versions of the texts were preceded by intermediate versions, which were them-selves drawn from basic documents, certain of which originated in various Pagan or Jewish communities that were at first quite distinct. This would explain the variation in tone that we find in the original preaching. Thus we see how an intermediate document influenced the final version of several Gospels, and it becomes clear that John undoubtedly remained the most individualistic author : His text deals with subjects that are quite different from those contained in the three other Gospels. Father Benoit is clearly aware of the doubts that these new approaches to the texts may engender in certain

---

1. According to the *Ecumenical Translation*, Luke contains 500 out of a total of 1,160 verses.
2. Published by Les Éditions du Cerf, Paris, 1972-1973.

people's minds : "Some readers of this work will perhaps be surprised or embarrassed to learn that certain of Jesus's sayings, parables, or predictions of His destiny were not expressed in the way we read them today, but were altered and adapted by those who transmitted them to us. This may come as a source of amazement and even scandal to those not used to this kind of historical investigation."

To return to the question previously raised concerning the genealogy of Jesus in the Gospels according to Luke, it is imperative to take into account the following fact when examining the discrepancy between Luke's Gospel and established reality : The evangelist presents his work as the result of a genuine inquiry, composed of the information he has gathered and which he intends to set forth. The following is Luke's own statement which appears in the prologue to his Gospel : "Inasmuch as many have undertaken to compile a narrative of the things which have been accomplished among us, just as they were delivered to us by those who from the beginning were eyewitnesses and ministers of the word, it seemed good to me also, having informed myself about all things from their beginnings, to write an orderly account for you, most excellent Theophilus, that you may know the truth concerning things of which you have been informed."

When Luke wishes to show that he and his community consider that Jesus was descended from Abraham and David, he turns for information to the Old Testament. There he finds a genealogy indicating the lineage of the first men from Adam to Abraham. Drawing his inspiration from tradition, Luke then proceeds to provide us with data on the time of man's first appearance on earth that are hopelessly wrong.

As we shall see in a moment, Matthew also makes a major error in his Gospel, for exactly the same reasons. While there is a strong possibility that Abraham lived between 1850-1800 B.C., or at least at roughly this period, Matthew records forty-one generations between Abraham and Jesus, a figure that for eighteen or nineteen centuries is a gross underestimation. Here again, we have an example of an evangelist adapting data from the Old Testament, and taking liberties in the process.

For our present purposes therefore, we may state that the inaccuracies discovered in the Gospels basically arise from errors in the Old Testament—more precisely in the Sacerdotal version that forms part of the Book of Genesis—which the evangelists merely repeated in their own works.

THE CREATION OF MAN ACCORDING
TO THE BIBLE:
THE NARRATIVES AND THEIR CONTEXT

In contrast to the Qur'an, the Bible does not contain statements on various natural phenomena which, at any time in man's history, could form the subject of observation and which might give rise to commentaries on God's omnipotence, accompanied by certain specific details. As we shall see later on, such texts are unique to the Qur'an; they are expressed in a form which permits us to compare many data with secular knowledge. The Bible confines itself to relating certain events from the past; the narrations it contains are peppered with details which, for one reason or another, interest the scientist on account of the fact that they either agree with or contradict data which are today firmly established or at least highly probable. While their number is small, I have mentioned several of them in 'La Bible, le Coran et la Science' [*The Bible, the Qur'an and Science*] for they nevertheless constitute points of considerable interest. In the Biblical narrative of the Flood, for example, we find in this description of a universal inundation, which in the Book of Genesis is precisely located in time, certain data which prevent us from considering that a cataclysm could have taken place on this scale at the period indicated. On the other hand, when we come to the narrative describing the Exodus, we find extremely valuable data, confirmed by Egyptian archaeology, which enable us to locate Moses in the history of the Pharaohs.

The Biblical accounts of the creation of man and the religious history of the first descendants of Adam and of the Jewish people, provided the Biblical authors with an opportunity to expand on two subjects which are of interest to us in the present work. The first is the origin of man, which is explicitly described in the Old Testament, and the second is the date of man's first appearance on earth. The latter is deduced from the numerical data contained in the Old Testament, which were provided for reasons other than to supply information directly related to the subject. In addition to this, although in a different guise, we find a reference to the subject in a work of the evangelists–the Gospel According to Luke.

The origins of man are explained in the Book of Genesis in the verses dealing with the Creation as a whole. In order to understand the subject properly, therefore, it must be placed in its proper context.

The Creation of Man According to Genesis

As acknowledged by Father de Vaux, Genesis "begins with two juxtaposed descriptions of the Creation." The existence of two texts must be stressed, for it is not generally known :

–the first is integrated into a text composed by the priests of the Temple at Jerusalem. It dates from the sixth century B.C., and is called the 'Sacerdotal' version. The longer of the two texts, it figures at the beginning of Genesis and forms part of the long narrative of the Creation of the heavens, the earth and living beings; the creation of man is emphasized as its crowning achievement, even though it is only briefly described;

–the second text is taken from the Yahvist version. It dates from the ninth or tenth century B.C. and is very short. It follows directly after the Sacerdotal version, and devotes more space to the creation of man. The text reproduced below is taken from the Revised Standard Version of the Bible [1] :

The first narrative (Genesis, the entire first chapter and chapter 2, verses 1 to 4a.) :

–Chapter One, verses 1 and 2 :

"In the beginning God created the heavens and the earth. The earth was without form and void, and darkness was upon the face of the deep; and the Spirit of God was moving over the face of the waters."

–Verses 3 to 5 :

"And God said, 'Let there be light', and there was light. And God saw that the light was good; and God separated the light from the darkness. God called the light Day, and the darkness he called Night. And there was evening and there was morning, one day."

1. Published by W.M. Collins and Sons for the British and Foreign Bible Society, 1952.

–Verses 6 to 8 :

"And God said, 'Let there be a firmament in the midst of the waters, and let it separate the waters from the waters'. And God made the firmament and separated the waters which were under the firmament from the waters which were above the firmament. And it was so. And God called the firmament Heaven. And there was evening and there was morning, a second day."

–Verses 9 to 13 :

"And God said, 'Let the waters under the heavens be gathered together into one place, and let the dry land appear.' And it was so. God called the dry land Earth, and the waters that were gathered together he called Seas. And God saw that it was good.

"And God said, 'Let the earth put forth vegetation, plants yielding seed, and fruit trees bearing fruit in which is their seed, each according to its kind upon the earth.' And it was so. The earth brought forth vegetation, plants yielding seed according to their own kinds, and trees bearing fruit in which is their seed, each according to its kind. And God saw that it was good. And there was evening and there was morning, a third day."

–Verses 14 to 19 :

"And God said, 'Let there be lights in the firmaments of the heavens to separate the day from the night; and let them be for signs and for seasons and for days and years, and let them be lights in the firmament of the heavens to give light upon the earth.' And it was so. And God made the two great lights, the greater light to rule the day, and the lesser light to rule the night; he made the stars also. And God set them in the firmament of the heavens to give light upon the earth, to rule over the day and over the night, and to separate the light from the darkness. And God saw that it was good. And there was evening and there was morning, a fourth day."

–Verses 20 to 23 :

"And God said, 'Let the waters bring forth swarms of living creatures, and let birds fly above the earth across the firmament of the heavens.' So God created the great sea monsters and every living creature that moves, with which the waters swam, according to their kinds, and every winged bird according to its kind. And God saw that it was good. And God blessed them saying, 'Be fruitful and multiply and fill the waters in the seas, and let birds multiply on the earth'. And there was evening and there was morning, a fifth day."

–Verses 24 to 31 :

"And God said, 'Let the earth bring forth living creatures according to their kinds : cattle and creeping things and beasts of the earth according to their kinds.' And it was so. And God made the beasts of the earth according to their kinds and the cattle according to their kinds, and everything that creeps upon the ground according to its kind. And God saw that it was good.

"Then God said, 'Let us make man in our image, after our likeness; and let them have dominion [sic] over the fish of the sea, and over the birds of the air, and over the cattle, and over all the earth and over every creeping thing that creeps upon the earth.'

"So God created man in his own image, in the image of God he created him; male and female he created them.

"And God blessed them, and God said to them, 'Be fruitful and multiply, and fill the earth and subdue it; and have dominion over the fish of the sea and over the birds of the air and over every living thing that moves upon the earth.' And God said, 'Behold, I have given you every plant yielding seed which is upon the face of all the earth, and every tree with seed in its fruit; you shall have them for food. And to every beast of the earth, and to every bird of the air, and to everything that creeps on the earth, everything that has the breath of life, I have given every green plant for food.' And it was so. And God saw everything that he had made, and behold, it was very good. And there was evening and there was morning, a sixth day."

–This narrative of the Creation comes to an end with verses 1 to 4a of Chapter Two :

"Thus the heavens and the earth were finished, and all the host [sic] of them. And on the seventh day God finished his work which he had done, and he rested on the seventh day from all his work which he had done. So God blessed the seventh day and hallowed it, because on it God rested from all his work which he had done in creation.

"These are the generations of the heavens and the earth when they were created."

The second narrative follows directly after the first :

–Chapter Two, verses 4b to 7 :

"In the day that Yahveh God [1] made the earth and heavens, when no plant of the field was yet in the earth and no herb of the field had yet sprung up–for Yahveh God had not caused it to rain upon the earth, and there was no man to till the ground; but a mist went up from the earth and watered the whole face of the ground–then Yahveh God formed man of dust from the ground, and breathed into

---

1. In this passage of the Revised Standard Version of the Bible, God is called 'the Lord God', whereas in older texts that served as works of reference, God is known as 'Yahveh God'. The name of the 'Yahvist Version' is derived from this fact. In the present work, the original name has been reinstated.

his nostrils the breath of life; and man became a living being."

There then follows a description of Earthly Paradise (verses 8 to 17) after which the narration continues with the creation of the animal kingdom and woman :

—Chapter Two, verses 18 to 25 :

"Then Yahveh God said, 'It is not good that the man should be alone; I will make him a helper fit for him.' So out of the ground Yahveh God formed every beast of the field and every bird of the air, and brought them to the man to see what he would call them; and whatever the man called every living creature, that was its name. The man gave names to all cattle, and to the birds of the air, and to every beast of the field; but for the man there was not found a helper fit for him. So Yahveh God caused a deep sleep to fall upon the man, and while he slept took one of his ribs and closed up its place with flesh; and the rib which Yahveh God had taken from the man he made into a woman and brought her to the man. Then the man said :

"'This at last is bone of my bones and flesh of my flesh; she shall be called Woman, because she was taken out of Man.'

"Therefore a man leaves his father and his mother and cleaves to his wife, and they become one flesh. And the man and his wife were both naked, and were not ashamed."

An Examination of the Two Narratives of the Creation in the Light of Modern Knowledge

The two narratives vary on more than one point : In particular, the origins of man and woman, whether mentioned or not, and, the order in which man appeared compared with the various species of animal. Furthermore, the sense attributed by the Bible to the creation of man cannot be understood in all its shades of meaning, within the same version, unless it is replaced in its general context; that is why the full text of the two narratives has been quoted above. In order for us to proceed to a comparison with established, or highly probable, data, we must first examine each text separately.

THE NARRATIVE FOUND IN THE SACERDOTAL VERSION

The image of the empty earth used in the first two verses to describe the state of the universe before the creation would simply seem to signify that creation started from the void. The Biblical author nevertheless devotes a place to the waters over which the spirit of God moved : We may perhaps be allowed to see in this a reference to the tradition of the 'primordial' waters, the source of all life.

The account of the first day (verses 3 to 5), and the description of the creation of light, along with the existence of an evening and a morning, suggest the following comments :

The light circulating in the universe is the result of complex reactions in the stars. At this stage in the Creation however, according to the Bible, the stars were not yet formed. The 'lights' of the firmament are not mentioned in Genesis until verse 14, when they were created on the fourth day, 'to separate the day from the night', 'to give light upon the earth'; all of which is quite accurate. It is illogical, however, to mention the result (light) on the first day, when the cause of this light ('two great lights') was created three days later. The fact that the existence of evening and morning is placed on the first day is, moreover, purely allegorical; the existence of evening and morning as elements of a single day is only conceivable after the creation of the earth and its rotation under the light of the sun.

The reference to a 'firmament' separating the waters (verses 6 to 8), on the second day, is a reflection of the ancient belief that a dome existed which contained the waters above the firmament : These were the waters which, in the narrative of the Flood, were to pass through the dome and fall in torrents on the earth.

The third day (verse 9 to 13) is devoted to the appearance of the dry land, once the waters had gathered together into one place–an idea that is perfectly acceptable. The third day also saw the earth put forth vegetation, in the form of trees bearing fruit–which is no longer acceptable at all, for vegetation requires sunlight, and the sun had not yet been formed. What is more, these verses contain a reference to the fixity of the vegetal species ("plants yielding seed according to their own kinds").

Verses 14 to 19 describe the creation of the sun and moon on the fourth day, after the creation of the earth on the third day. Our modern knowledge of the formation of the solar system does not allow us to state that the sun became a luminous star after the earth came into being, as it is claimed in the Bible. The origins of the sun and moon cannot be separated from those of the earth.

The first representatives of the animal kingdom, which according to verses 20 to 23 populated the seas and sky on the fifth day, are described in terms that suggest that they came before the existence of terrestrial animals, which did not appear until the sixth day. There is good reason to think that the origins of life are indeed aquatic and that the dry land was 'colonized' later on. Nevertheless, the Bible states that the birds existed before the terrestrial animals, whereas in fact the birds appeared after a certain group of reptiles : The birds came after the mammals, and were the very last group to appear. This therefore constitutes a case of a statement contradicting the established data of paleontology.

According to the narrative (verses 24 to 31), the earth brought forth terrestrial animals on the sixth day, and although his origin is not specified, man was created by God in His own image on that day. Woman was also created, though no details are given concerning her origins. This contrasts with the Yahvist version, which predates the Sacerdotal text, in which man's origins are described–he was formed from the ground–and those of woman created from man. He is placed at the pinnacle of creation with dominion over the rest of the animal kingdom. The fixity of species is emphasized in the case of the terrestrial animals, just as it had been stressed with regard to the marine animals created on the fifth day.

The Sacerdotal version judiciously places man's appearance on earth after that of the other categories of living beings, but, as we have noted for the rest of the animal kingdom, the order of appearance described in the narrative does not conform to the clearly proven facts of paleontology.

The account of the seventh day refers to God's day of rest, for that is the meaning of the Hebrew word 'Shabbath'; this is the origin of the Jewish day of rest, known as the 'Sabbath'.

The division of God's labour of creation into six days followed by a day of rest is not without explanation. We should bear in mind that the description of the Creation examined here is taken from the so-called 'Sacerdotal' version, written by priests and scribes who were the spiritual successors of Ezekiel, the prophet of the exile in Babylon, writing in the sixth century B.C. The priests took the Yahvist and Elohist versions of Genesis and remodelled them after their own fashion, in accordance with their theological and liturgical preoccupations. Father de Vaux has noted that the 'legalist' character of these writings was absolutely essential.

The Yahvist version of the Creation, which appeared at least three centuries before the Sacerdotal text, indeed makes no reference whatsoever to God's Sabbath, to any question of days, or to the phases of the Creation, judging from what remains of the text today. On the other hand, the Sacerdotal version divides the Creation into days. There can be absolutely no doubt as to the meaning of these days, because for each day, we are reminded that there was an evening and a morning. We are also told that the Creation took place over a period of six days, with a seventh day of rest, known as the 'Sabbath'. There is good reason to think that this is an example of a narrative written with the aim of inciting people to respect the religious observance of the Sabbath, a fundamental aspect of Judaism. We should therefore view the Sacerdotal version first and foremost as a text designed to influence religious rites, without any claim to set down events with the rigorous accuracy of a historian.

THE NARRATIVE FOUND
IN THE YAHVIST VERSION

The creation of the earth and the heavens is only mentioned once in this version, for the text primarily deals with man.

It begins with a statement that does not square with modern knowledge of the history of the earth : The absence of any vegetation at the moment God created man. "Yahveh God had not caused it to rain upon the earth and there was no man to till the ground."

The narrative stresses the fact that God formed man of dust from the ground. Hence in this instance, man's origin from the earth is emphasized, with all the symbolical significance this origin suggests. None of this is mentioned in the more recent Sacerdotal text, examined above.

As for the origins of the animals, the Revised Standard Version of the Bible (1952) simply states that "Yahveh God formed every beast of the field and every bird of the air" (verse 19) without saying where they came from. In contrast, the 'Traduction Œcuménique de la Bible' *[Ecumenical Translation of the Bible]*, states quite clearly in the French text that "God again moulded from the ground all the wild beasts and the birds of the air". Thus, according to the French version, all living beings, man and animals, were formed from· the ground. Neither the English nor the French translation seems to provide an exact period for the appearance of the animals as compared with the creation of man [1].

The final verses refer to the creation of woman from a part of man's body, a detail which the Sacerdotal version does not record.

The Yahvist version is distinguished by its *symbolism*, for its author emphasizes the formation of man from the ground. This symbolism is present even in the choice of vocabulary : The name of the very first man, 'Adam', is in fact a collective noun in Hebrew

---

1. The two Biblical texts mention the fact that God "brought them to the man to see what he would call them", but that does not mean to say that the animals were created either before or after man.

meaning 'man'. The word comes from *'adamah'* which means
'ground', for man is indeed dependent on the ground for his
existence. There is however another symbolical meaning present,
which is repeated in other parts of the Bible as well. In Ecclesiastes
(3, 19 and 20), the Biblical author stresses the common destiny of the
sons of Adam and of all living beings : "... All go to one place; all are
from the dust, and all turn to dust again." Man's return to the ground
is repeated in Psalm 104 (verse 29), and we find the same idea
present in the Book of Job (34, 15).

A profound religious meaning is therefore inherent in these
Biblical reflections on man's fate after death. In the Yahvist version
of Genesis, it is introduced by the notion of a place of origin which is
also the place of return after death. This specifically religious
concept must not be confused with the narration of material events
from which no precise religious meaning is to be inferred.

We must bear in mind that in their day, the Biblical authors could
only express themselves in images that would be readily understood.
They were obliged to use the language of their period and to refer to
the traditions current at the time they wrote. If we compare the two
versions–the Yahvist version pre-dating the Sacerdotal text by three
hundred, if not four hundred years–, we shall see the difference
between them quite clearly : The view-point expressed by the
authors of the more recent (Sacerdotal) text has changed. This fact
emerges in spite of any legitimate doubts we may entertain as to
whether the texts we possess today are the same as the ones written
at the time. Additions may have been made, and there may also have
been sections cut from the texts : It is astonishing to note that in the
Yahvist version, the earth and the heavens are referred to in simple
terms, without any mention of the actual way in which they were
created.

Right up until the age of science, the text of the Creation
contained in the Book of Genesis was the only acknowledged
historical source of information on the events leading to the
appearance on earth of man and living beings. In days gone by, the
Biblical text was therefore considered to be a basic point of
reference. When naturalists wished to harmonize the ideas that arose
from an examination of the first discovered fossils with the teachings
of the Bible on the fixity of the species, they imagined that the
existence of the flora and fauna found in extremely ancient terranes
could only be explained by the intervention of successive cataclysms,
such as the Flood, which must have destroyed everything and been
followed by new creations. This is what Cuvier thought at the
beginning of the nineteenth century. The influence of these theories

persisted long after Cuvier, for in 1862, Alcide d'Orbigny mentions twenty-seven successive creations following repeated cataclysms!

It is in fact an error to suppose that the Flood, as described in the Bible, destroyed absolutely everything on earth *at a certain period.* According to the Biblical narratives, there most definitely *was* a universal cataclysm, but it nevertheless spared a few human beings. The latter found refuge with Noah in the Ark, and with them the animals belonging to the species that had entered it. The earth is said to have been repopulated by the animals and humans who were thus able to escape the Flood. The Bible does not, however, speak of the newly created species which were later to appear.

The Date of Man's First Appearance on Earth

The Bible deals with this subject in two different ways : First, it provides us with the genealogical tables of the earliest men, in which we find figures indicating the duration of their lives, and second, it supplies us with the number of the generations that intervened between Adam and the birth of Jesus.

DATA FROM THE BIBLICAL GENEALOGIES

The Jewish calendar is the most authoritative source in this instance, for it is based on Biblical as well as non-Biblical sources. The calendar starts with the Creation, which it states took place 5,742 years ago (counting from the last third of A.D. 1981). Calculated according to the traditional Jewish calendar, man therefore appeared on earth 5,742 years ago—a statement that quite obviously contradicts reality.

Leaving aside the data contained in the calendar, it is possible to arrive at an extremely accurate estimate of the time separating Adam from Abraham, using as sole source the Biblical text and taking into account the period at which Abraham most probably lived [1]. In this manner, it is possible to arrive at the approximate date of man's first appearance on earth according to the two sources. The Bible does not in fact provide numerical genealogies that continue uninterrupted beyond the period of the Patriarchs.

Genesis supplies extremely precise genealogical data in chapters 4, 5, 11, 21 and 25. They concern every one of Abraham's

---

1. According to certain details contained in the Bible (Father de Vaux, 'Histoire Ancienne d'Israël' *(The History of Ancient Israel),* published by J. Gabalda et Cie, Paris, 1971.

ancestors in direct line back to Adam. They give the length of time each person lived and the father's age at the birth of the son. Thus it is easy to ascertain the dates of birth and death of each ancestor in relation to the creation of Adam. As we already know, the genealogies ascribe to Abraham and his nineteen ancestors back to Adam lifespans that are incredibly long : In the case of Methuselah, the figure is 969 years, compared to which the lifespan of Abraham was a mere 175 years! Once all these data have been assembled and the lifespans have been added together as each successive generation appeared, the conclusion to be drawn from the Bible is that Abraham, who was born 1,948 years after Adam could theoretically have known Noah (born 1,056 years after Adam and who died 2,006 years after him), and that in similar fashion, Lemek, who was Noah's father, could have known Adam! The Biblical genealogies referred to here were compiled by priests of the sixth century B.C. By citing abnormally long lifespans, the priests may have hoped thereby to express the idea of divine omnipotence.

Theoretically, one might suggest a correction, for time was originally calculated in lunar years, whereas today's calendar is based on solar years. Since the difference between them is only 3 % or thirty years per millenium, however, it is so minimal that it is not worth considering.

At what period should we situate Abraham? Present-day estimates indicate that he probably lived in either the eighteenth or the nineteenth century B.C. If we accept the second estimate, and combine it with detailed Biblical data on the interval separating Adam from Abraham, according to the Bible, we should situate Adam at a period near the thirty-eighth century B.C. This estimate is in perfect harmony with the data contained in the Biblical calendar. We may therefore conclude that man's appearance on the sixth day of Creation—as related in the Sacerdotal version—must have occurred during the thirty-seventh or thirty-eighth century B.C. : expressed in round figures, fifty-seven of fifty-eight centuries before our own period. It is to be noted that the Yahvist version of Genesis does not contain any numerical data on which to base this estimate.

Older editions of the Bible often contained their own chronological tables which tended to vary from one edition to another : the famous Walton Bible, for example, which was published in London in 1657. This edition, which was distinguished by the fact that it contained Hebrew, Greek, Latin, Syriac, Aramean and even Arabic versions, presented numerical estimates that were more or less in agreement with the data cited above. The *Vulgate Clementine,* a Vulgate edition of the Bible, published in 1621, situates Abraham at a slightly earlier period, placing the Creation at roughly the fortieth century B.C. This estimate was for many years used as the basic point of reference in the teachings of the Catholic Church.

Genesis states that the universe and man were both created within the same week. If we wish to compare this statement with modern knowledge, however, it is difficult to refer to precise data concerning the period in which the universe was created, for present knowledge on this subject is somewhat approximate. This is not the case, however, for the solar system. Here, the age of the earth has been estimated at some 4.5 billion years, with a margin of error of some one hundred million years. As for man's first appearance on earth, we shall simply recall the fact that some 40,000 years ago, a man exactly similar to present-day man was already in existence, while less evolved forms of hominids have been found which—in the present state of research—most probably go back some five million years. It is not possible to provide definitive figures, for the discoveries made by paleontology are subject to change, but we know for certain that men with fully developed brains were already in existence at a period far in advance of the era considered by the Sacerdotal version of Genesis to be that of man's first appearance on earth.

DATA CONTAINED IN THE NEW TESTAMENT

Matthew's and Luke's Gospels both contain a genealogy of Jesus; the first traces His ancestors back to Abraham, and the second provides a line that goes back to Adam. Both of them are in fact genealogies of Joseph—who had absolutely nothing to do with the birth of Jesus—which renders the genealogies illogical, to say the least. The two evangelists in fact based their texts on data in the Old Testament, which they arranged to suit their own purposes, thus taking liberties with the Biblical Scripture—Matthew in particular—which explains the notable differences that exist between the two genealogies.

The genealogy which interests us the most is the one according to Luke (3, 23-38) which contains seventy-six names of ancestors of Jesus, going back to Adam. Earlier, we said that the average lifespan of a human generation was roughly estimated at twenty-five years; this would mean that Adam was situated at the beginning of the second millenium B.C., which is simply not possible. Even if we take into consideration the period of some two thousand years that the Bible attributes to twenty generations descending from Adam to Abraham, we are still a very long way from the data supplied by paleontology (described earlier) concerning the date of man's appearance on earth.

A comparison of the names which appear in Luke's text and the data contained in the Bible indicates that, in many instances, the list supplied by Luke does not agree with the information set forth in the oldest copies of the Bible. Names have been added by Luke to fill the gaps between the groups of genuine descendants of David– mentioned in the Old Testament – and Joseph. Scattered through Luke's text, we find names corresponding to those of the descendants of David which figure in Matthew's text. For this same period of time, however, Matthew mentions twenty-six names, while Luke refers to forty-one.

It is possible that Matthew and Luke did not possess the same source material from the Old Testament. Whatever the case, both of them used their sources with the evident intention of showing that Jesus was descended from Abraham and David. It is a pity that Luke went even further than this, for his total of seventy-six generations between Jesus and the first man is totally implausible.

The Inevitability of Scientific Error in the Bible

Luke, and indeed the authors of the Old Testament, composed their texts using the sources at their disposal, drawing on the traditions they had inherited, and expressing themselves in the language of their time. All of them were motivated by an essentially religious aim; they naturally had no other intention than to transmit ideas which, in their eyes, carried a basically religious meaning. In view of this, it would be a misreading of the purpose of the Bible to search through its books in the hope of finding any scientific data whatsoever that might be usable in practical terms. This applies, moreover, to all the Holy Scriptures.

In this context, the fact that there are errors in the Bible was inevitable. How could the men of the period have failed to make such blunders? They most definitely had no access to the information required for them to refer to events–such as those discussed in the present work–without committing mistakes. An extremely relevant comment on this subject is made by Jean Guitton in 'Mon petit catéchisme' *[My Little Catechism],* published in 1978. It reads as follows : "The scientific errors in the Bible are the errors of mankind, for long ago man was like a child, as yet ignorant of science." Neither Jews nor Christians should be surprised, embarrassed or shocked to find scientific errors in the Bible. It would indeed have been most astounding had there been no inaccurate statements, considering the circumstances present when the Biblical books were written. Until very recently, those circumstances were unkown, for any commentary on the text of the Bible which might cast doubt on the fact that God was its indirect author was judged intolerable by the various Churches. Nowadays, however, the discovery of scientific errors is in perfect keeping with the ideas of exegetes–Christian exegetes, at least. They regard the Biblical authors as writers who, while undoubtedly inspired by God, nevertheless expressed themselves in the language of their day, in the absence of any serious scientific knowledge. Thus we come back to the point originally made at the beginning of this section : One has to know the history of the texts in order to arrive at a valid assessment of their contents.

IV

THE ORIGIN, TRANSFORMATIONS AND REPRODUCTION OF MAN ACCORDING TO THE QUR'AN

PRELIMINARY NOTIONS
ON THE QUR'ANIC TEXT,
ITS HISTORY AND CONTENTS

Those unaware of the position occupied by the Qur'an as compared with the Bible, or who remain ignorant of the circumstances in which the Qur'an was communicated to man will no doubt be astonished to find so much space devoted in this study to the Qur'anic text. Their amazement may be explained by the fact that most people in the West have been brought up on misconceptions concerning Islam and the Qur'an; for a large part of my life, I myself was one such person. Let me cite one or two specific examples to indicate the kind of inaccurate ideas generally current.

As I grew up, I was always taught that 'Mahomet' was the author of the Qur'an; I remember seeing French translations bearing this information. I was invariably told that the 'author of the Qur'an' simply compiled, in a slightly different form, stories of sacred history taken from the Bible; the 'author' was said to have added or removed certain passages, while setting forth the principles and rules of the religion he himself had founded. There are moreover Islamic scholars today in France whose duties include teaching and who express exactly these views, although perhaps in a more subtle form.

This description of the origins of the Qur'anic text, which is so out of touch with reality, might lead one immediately to assume that if there are scientific errors in the Bible, then there must also be errors of this kind in the Qur'an! This is the natural conclusion to be drawn in such circumstances, but it is based on a misconception. We are well aware that at the time of Muhammed—the Qur'anic Revelation took place between 610 and 632 A.D.—scientific obscurantism prevailed, both in the Orient as well as in the West. In France, for example, this period corresponded roughly to the reign of King Dagobert, the last of the Merovingians. This approach to what was

supposedly the Qur'anic text may on first sight seem logical, but
when one examines the text with an informed and impartial eye, it
becomes clear that this approach is not at all in keeping with reality.
We shall see in a moment the truth of this statement, which is
obvious from the texts.

Whenever there is textual proof of the existence in the Qur'an of
statements that are in agreement with modern knowledge, but which
in the Bible are related in a manner that is scientifically unacceptable, the stock response is that, during the period separating the two
Scriptures, Arab scientists made discoveries in various disciplines
which enabled them to arrive at these supposed adaptations. This
approach takes no account whatsoever of the history of the sciences.
The latter indicates that the great period of Islamic civilization,
during which, as we know, science made considerable progress, came
several centuries *after* the communication of the Qur'an to man.
Furthermore, scientific history informs us that, as far as the subjects
dealt with in this present book are concerned, no discoveries were
made during the period separating the Bible from the Qur'an.

When this aspect of the Qur'an is mentioned in the West, however,
we are likely to hear it said that while this may indeed be so, nowhere
is this fact referred to in the translations of the Qur'an which we
possess today, or in the prefaces and commentaries that accompany
them.

This is a very judicious remark. Muslim–and indeed non-
Muslim–translators who have produced a French version of the
Qur'an are basically men of letters. More often than not, they
mistranslate a passage because they do not possess the scientific
knowledge required to understand its true meaning. The fact is,
however, that in order to translate correctly, one must first
understand what one is reading. A further point is that translators–
especially those mentioned above–may have been influenced by
notes provided by ancient commentators to explain the text. By force
of tradition, such commentators often came to be regarded as highly
authoritative, even though they had no scientific knowledge–nor
indeed had anybody else at the time. They were incapable of
imagining that the texts might contain allusions to secular knowledge, and thus they could not devote attention to a specific passage
by comparing it to other verses in the Qur'an dealing with the same
subject–a process that often provides the key to the meaning of a
word or expression. From this results the fact that any passage in the
Qur'an that gives rise to a comparison with modern secular
knowledge is likely to be unreliably translated. Very often, the
translations are peppered with inaccurate–if not totally nonsensical–

statements. The only way to avoid committing such errors is to possess a scientific background and to study the Qur'anic text in the original language.

It was not until I had learnt Arabic and read the Qur'an in the original that I realized the precise meaning of certain verses. Only then did I make certain discoveries that were astounding. With my basic ideas on the Qur'an–which to begin with were inaccurate, just as those of most people in the West–, I certainly did not expect to find in the text the statements that I in fact uncovered. With each new discovery, I was beset with doubt lest I might be mistaken in my translation or perhaps have provided an interpretation rather than a true rendering of the Arabic text. Only after consultations with several specialists in linguistics and exegesis, both Muslim and non-Muslim, was I convinced that a new concept might be formed from such a study : the compatibility between the statements in the Qur'an and the firmly established data of modern science with regard to subjects on which nobody at the time of Muhammad–not even the Prophet himself–could have had access to the knowledge we possess today. Since then, I have not found in the Qur'an any support given to the myths or superstitions present at the time the text was communicated to man. This is not the case for the Bible, whose authors expressed themselves in the language of their period.

In 'La Bible, le Coran et la Science' [*The Bible, the Qur'an and Science*], which first appeared in the original French in 1976 and which subsequently appeared in English in 1978, I set forth the main points of these findings. On November 9, 1976, I gave a lecture to the Académie de Médecine [French Academy of Medecine] in which I explored the statements on the origins of man contained in the Qur'an; the title of the lecture was 'Données physiologiques et embryologiques du Coran' [*Physiological and Embryological Data in the Qur'an*] [1]. I emphasized the fact that these data–which I shall summarize below–formed part of a much wider study. The following are some of the points which arise from a reading of the Qur'an :

–a concept of the creation of the world which, while different from the ideas contained in the Bible, is fully in keeping with today's general theories on the formation of the universe;

–statements that are in perfect agreement with today's ideas concerning the movements and evolution of the heavenly bodies;

–a prediction of the conquest of space;

1. Published in « Bulletin de l'Académie Nationale de Médecine », 160, 734-737, 1976.

–notions concerning the water cycle in nature and the earth's relief, which were not proven correct until many centuries later.

All of these data are bound to amaze anyone who approaches them in an objective spirit. They add a much wider dimension to the problem studied in the present work. The basic point remains the same, however : we must surely be in the presence of facts which place a heavy strain on our natural propensity for explaining everything in materialistic terms, for the existence in the Qur'an of these scientific statements appears as a challenge to human explanation.

On the subject of man, as well as the other topics mentioned earlier, it is not possible to find any corresponding data in the Bible. Furthermore, the scientific errors contained in the Bible–such as those describing man's first appearance on earth, which, as we have seen, may be deduced from the genealogies that figure in Genesis– are not to be found in the Qur'an. It is crucial to understand that such errors could not have been 'edited out' of the Qur'an since the time they first became apparent : Well over a thousand years have elapsed since the most ancient manuscripts and today's texts of the Qur'an, but the texts are still absolutely identical. Thus, if Muhammad were the author of the Qur'an (a theory upheld by some people), it is difficult to see how he could have spotted the scientific errors in the Bible dealing with such a wide variety of subjects and have proceeded to eliminate *every single one of them* when he came to compose his own text on the same themes. Let us state once again, that no new scientific facts had been discovered since the time the Bible was written that might have helped eliminate such errors.

In view of the above, it is imperative to know the history of the texts, just as it is essential to our understanding of certain aspects of the Bible for us to be aware of the conditions in which it was written.

As we have noted earlier, experts in Biblical exegesis consider the books of the Old and New Testaments to be divinely inspired works. Let us now examine, however, the teachings of Muslim exegetes, who present the Qur'an in quite a different fashion.

When Muhammad was roughly forty years old, it was his custom to retire to a retreat just outside Mecca in order to meditate. It was here that he received a first message from God via the Angel Gabriel, at a date that corresponds to 610 A.D. After a long period of silence, this first message was followed by successive revelations spread over some twenty years. During the Prophet's lifetime, they were both written down and recited by heart among his first followers. Similarly, the revelations were divided into suras (chapters) and collected together after the Prophet's death (in 632 A.D.)

in a book : the Qur'an. The Book contains the Word of God, to the exclusion of any human additions. Manuscripts dating from the first century of Islam authenticate today's text, the other form of authentification being the recitation by heart of the Qur'an, a practice that has continued unbroken from the time of the Prophet down to the present day.

In contrast to the Bible, therefore, we are here presented with a text that is none other than the transcript of the Revelation itself; the only way it can be received and interpreted is literally. The purity of the revealed text has been greatly emphasized, and the uncorrupted nature of the Qur'an stems from the following factors :

First, as stated above, fragments of the text were written down during the Prophet's lifetime; inscribed on tablets, parchments and other materials current at the time. The Qur'an itself refers to the fact that the text was set down in writing. We find this in several suras dating from before and after the Hegira (Muhammad's departure from Mecca to Medina in 622 A.D.) In addition to the transcription of the text, however, there was also the fact that it was learned by heart. The text of the Qur'an is much shorter than the Old Testament and slightly longer than the New Testament. Since it took twenty years for the Qur'an to be revealed, however, it was easy for the Prophet's followers to recite it by heart, sura by sura. This process of recitation afforded a considerable advantage as far as an uncorrupted text was concerned, for it provided a system of double-checking at the time the definitive text was written down. This took place several years after the Prophet's death; first under the caliphate of Abu Bakr, his first successor, and later under the caliphate of Omar and in particular that of Uthman (644 to 655 A.D.) The latter ordered an extremely strict recension of the text, which involved checking it against the recited version.

After Muhammad's death, Islam rapidly expanded far beyond the limits of the area in which it was born. Soon, it included many peoples whose native language was not Arabic. Very strict steps were taken to ensure that the text of the Qur'an did not suffer from this expansion of Islam : Uthman sent copies of his entire recension to the principal centres of the vast Islamic empire. Some copies still exist today, in more or less complete form, in such places as Tashkent (U.S.S.R.) and Istanbul. Copies have also been discovered that date from the very first centuries after the Hegira; they are all indentical, and all of them correspond to the earliest manuscripts. Today's editions of the Qur'an are all faithful reproductions of the original copies. In the case of the Qur'an, there are no instances of rewriting or corruptions of the text over the course of time.

If the origins of the Qur'an had been similar to those of the Bible, it would not be unreasonable to suppose that the subjects it raised would be presented in the light of ideas influenced by certain opinions of the time, often derived from myth and superstition. If this were the case, one might also assume that the text was full of statements reflecting varied traditions whose origins are often obscure. Furthermore, one might argue that there were untold opportunities for inaccurate assertions, based on such sources, to find their way into the many and varied subjects briefly summarized above. In actual fact, however, we find nothing of the kind in the Qur'an.

But having said this, we should note that the Qur'an is a religious book *par excellence.* We should not use statements that have a bearing on secular knowledge as a pretext to go hunting after any expression of scientific laws. As stated earlier, all we should seek are reflections on natural phenomena, phrases occasioned by references to divine omnipotence and designed to emphasize that omnipotence in the eyes of mankind throughout the ages. The presence of such reflections in the Qur'an has become particularly significant in modern times, for their meaning is clearly explained by the data of contemporary knowledge. This characteristic is specific to the Qur'an.

That does not mean to say, however, that the statements in the Qur'an–especially those concerning man–may *all of them* be examined in the light of the findings of modern science. The creation of man as described in both the Bible and the Qur'an totally eludes scientific investigation of the event *per se.* Similarly, when the New Testament or the Qur'an informs us that Jesus was not born of a father, in the biological sense of the term, we cannot counter this Scriptural statement by saying that there is no example in the human species of an individual having been formed without receiving the paternal chromosomes that make up one half of its genetic inheritance : Science does not explain miracles, for by definition, miracles are inexplicable. Thus, when we read in both the Qur'an and the Bible that man was moulded from the ground, we are in fact learning a fundamental religious principle : Man returns from whence he came, for from the place where he is buried, he will rise again on the Day of Judgement.

Side by side with the main religious aspect of such reflections on man, we find in the Qur'an statements on man that refer to strictly material facts. They are quite amazing when one approaches them for the first time. For example, the Qur'an describes the origins of life in general and devotes a great deal of space to the morphological transformations undergone by man, repeadly emphasizing the fact that God fashioned him as he willed. We likewise discover statements on human reproduction that are expressed in precise terms that lend themselves to comparison with the secular knowledge we today possess on the subject.

The many statements in the Qur'an that may thus be compared with modern knowledge are by no means easy to find. In preparing the study published in 1976, I was unable to draw on any previous works known in the West, for there were none. All I could refer to were a few works in Arabic dealing with themes treated in the Qur'an that were of interest to men of science–there was, however, no overall study. Over and above this, research of this kind requires scientific knowledge covering many different disciplines. It is not easy, however, for Islamologists to acquire such knowledge, for they possess a mainly literary background. Indeed, such questions hardly seem to occupy a place in the field of classic Islamology, at least as far as the West is concerned. Only a scientist, thoroughly acquainted with Arabic literature, can draw comparisons between the Qur'anic text–for which he must be able to read Arabic–and the data supplied by modern knowledge.

There is another reason why such statements are not immediately apparent : Verses bearing on a single theme are scattered throughout the Qur'an. The Book is indeed a juxtaposition of reflections on a wide variety of subjects referred to one after the other and taken up again later on, often several times over. The data on a precise theme must therefore be collected from all over the Book and brought together under a single heading. This requires many hours'work tracking down verses, in spite of the existence of thematic indexes provided by various translators, for such lists may perhaps be incomplete and indeed, in many cases, they often are.

In the present study, I have based my observations on facts and have presented the logical deductions necessarily to be drawn from them. This means that if I had not carried out this research, sooner or later, others would have performed it in my place. The study represents an innovation in the examination of a Holy Scripture, especially as far as readers in the West are concerned. Indeed, the latter are accustomed to separating texts which, when they approach them for the first time, seem to deal more with faith–any faith–than with reason; in their eyes, a study of the texts does not immediately suggest the need to refer to scientific data. As we have already seen in the case of the Bible, however, scientific data can indeed be included in an analysis of the text; the reader will quickly realize that a textual examination of the Qur'an requires even greater

164

The Qur'an

recourse to scientific evidence. The reason for this is the large
number of comparisons which must be made; for in this context, the
Qur'an contains a wealth of statements, even on the subject of man, a
topic that is fairly limited compared to the wide range of other
themes dealt with in the Qur'an.

THE ORIGIN AND PERPETUATION OF LIFE

One of the original features of the Qur'an that distinguishes it from the Bible is that, as mentioned above, in order to illustrate the repeated affirmations of divine omnipotence, the Book refers to a multitude of natural phenomena. In the case of a large number of these phenomena, it also provides a detailed description of the way they evolved, their causes and their effects; all of these details are worthy of attention. The statements on man contained in the Qur'an were among those which struck me the most when I read the Book of the first time in the original Arabic. Only the original can cast light on the real meaning of statements which are so often mistranslated, owing to the reasons cited above.

What makes these findings so important is that they refer to many notions which were not current at the time the Qur'an was communicated to man and which—fourteen centuries later—are evidently in perfect harmony with modern knowledge. In this context, there is absolutely no need to look for the kind of bogus explanations that tend to crop up in certain publications, and even in histories of medicine, in which Muhammad is claimed to possess medical skills (just as the Qur'an is also said to contain medical 'recipes', an idea that is totally inaccurate).[1]

---

1. All the Qur'an contains are certain dictates concerning hygiene and dietary habits : personal cleanliness, dietary interdicts such as the prohibition of alcohol; a dictate such as the fast of Ramadan also forms an obvious part of these rules. The mention of honey in the Qur'an does not include any indication of specific cases in which honey might prove beneficial to human health.

The Origins of Life

The Qur'an provides a clear-cut answer to the question : At what point did life begin? In this section, I shall set forth the verses of the Qur'an in which it is stated that the origins of life are aquatic. The first verse also refers to the formation of the universe :

–Sura 21, verse 30 :

أَوَلَمْ يَرَ ٱلَّذِينَ كَفَرُوٓاْ أَنَّ ٱلسَّمَـٰوَٰتِ وَٱلْأَرْضَ كَانَتَا
رَتْقًا فَفَتَقْنَـٰهُمَا ۖ وَجَعَلْنَا مِنَ ٱلْمَآءِ كُلَّ شَىْءٍ حَىٍّ
أَفَلَا يُؤْمِنُونَ

"Do not the Unbelievers see that the heavens and the earth were joined together, then We clove them asunder and We got every living thing out of water. Will they then not believe?"

The notion of 'getting something out of something else' does not give rise to any doubts. The phrase can equally mean that every living thing was made of water (as its essential component) or that every living thing originated in water. The two possible meanings are strictly in accordance with scientific data. Life is in fact of aquatic origin and water is the major component of all living cells. Without water, life is not possible. When the possibility of life on another planet is discussed, the first question is always : Is there a sufficient quantity of water to support life?

Modern data lead us to think that the oldest living beings probably belonged to the vegetable kingdom : Algae have been found that date from the pre-Cambrian period, the time of the oldest known lands. Organisms belonging to the animal kingdom probably appeared slightly later : They too came from the sea.

The word translated here as 'water' is in fact *mâ'* [1], which means both water in the sky and water in the sea, or any kind of liquid. In the first meaning, water is the element necessary to all vegetal life :

---

1. Readers requiring further information on the transliteration of the Arabic into Latin characters are advised to consult the chart that appears in *The Bible, the Qur'an and Science* (French Edition).

–Sura 20, verse 53 :

$$\text{وَأَنزَلَ مِنَ ٱلسَّمَآءِ مَآءً فَأَخْرَجْنَا بِهِۦٓ أَزْوَٰجًا مِّن}$$

$$\text{نَّبَاتٍ شَتَّىٰ}$$

"[God is the One who] sent water down from the sky and thereby We [1] brought forth pairs of plants each separate from the other."

This is the first reference to a 'pair' of vegetals; we shall have cause to return to this notion later.

In the second meaning, which refers to any kind of liquid, the word is used in its indeterminate form to designate the substance at the basis of the formation of all animal life :

–Sura 24, verse 45 :

$$\text{وَٱللَّهُ خَلَقَ كُلَّ دَآبَّةٍ مِّن مَّآءٍ}$$

"God created every animal from water."

As we shall see later on, the word may also be applied to seminal liquid [2].

Thus the statements in the Qur'an on the origins of life, whether referring to life in general, the element that gives birth to the plants in the soil, or the seed of animals, are all strictly in accordance with modern scientific data. None of the myths on the origins of life that abounded at the time the Qur'an was communicated to man are mentioned in the text.

The Perpetuation of Life

The Qur'an refers to many aspects of life in the animal and vegetable kingdoms. I have already described them in my previous work, published in 1976 (English edition 1978). In the present study, I should like to focus on the space given in the Qur'an to the theme of the perpetuation of life.

1. This change in the grammatical structure of a phrase is a common feature in the Qur'an. God is first referred to indirectly, then the text relates His direct Words, for 'We' obviously means God.
2. Secreted by the reproductive glands, seminal liquid contains the spermatozoa.

Generally speaking, the commentaries devoted to reproduction in
the vegetable kingdom are longer than those referring to animal
reproduction; when it comes to human reproduction, however, there
are many statements dealing with this theme, as we shall see.

It has been established that there are two methods of reproduction
in the vegetable kingdom : sexual and asexual (for example, the
multiplication of spores, or the process of taking cuttings, which is a
special case of growth). It is noteworthy that the Qur'an refers to
male and female parts of the vegetals :

–Sura 20, verse 53 :

$$\text{وَأَنزَلَ مِنَ ٱلسَّمَاءِ مَاءً فَأَخْرَجْنَا بِهِۦٓ أَزْوَٰجًا مِّن}$$

$$\text{نَّبَاتٍ شَتَّىٰ}$$

"[God is the One who] sent water down from the sky and thereby
We brought forth pairs of plants each separate from the other."

'One of a pair' is the translation of *zawj* (plural *azwâj*) whose
original meaning is 'that which, in the company of another, forms a
pair.' The word may just as readily be applied to a married couple as
to a pair of shoes.

–Sura 13, verse 3 :

$$\text{وَمِن كُلِّ ٱلثَّمَرَٰتِ جَعَلَ فِيهَا زَوْجَيْنِ ٱثْنَيْنِ}$$

"Of all fruits [God] placed [on earth] two of a pair."

This statement implies the existence of male and female organs in
all the various species of fruit. It is in perfect agreement with the
data discovered at a much later period concerning the formation of
fruit, for every type comes from vegetals possessing sexual organs
(even if certain varieties, such as the banana, originate from
non-fertilized flowers).

By and large, sexual reproduction in the animal kingdom is given
only brief treatment in the Qur'an. The exception to this is man, for
as we shall see in the following chapter, the statements on this
subject are numerous and detailed.

THE ORIGIN OF MAN AND TRANSFORMATIONS
OF THE HUMAN FORM OVER THE AGES

Some of the verses of the Qur'an which are to follow do not contain anything but a deeply spiritual meaning. Others, it would seem to me, refer to transformations that appear to indicate changes in human morphology. The latter describe phenomena of a totally material kind which occured in different phases but always *in the proper order*. The supreme intervention of divine will is mentioned several times in these verses. It is seen to direct the transformations which occur during a process that can only be described as an 'evolution'. Here, the word is used to mean a series of modifications whose purpose is to arrive at a definitive form. Furthermore, the accent is laid on the idea that God's omnipotence is manifest in the fact that He annihilated human populations to make way for new ones : These seem to me to constitute the main themes that arise from the collection of Qur'anic verses brought together in this chapter.

There can be no doubt that ancient commentators could not possibly have conceived of the idea that the human form might be transformed. They were willing, however, to admit that changes could indeed take place, and they acknowledged the existence of stages in the course of embryonic development—a phenomenon commonly observed in all periods of history. It is only in our own day, however, that modern knowledge allows us fully to understand the meaning of the verses in the Qur'an which refer to the successive phases of embryonic development within the uterus.

Indeed, we may today wonder whether the references in the Qur'an to the successive stages of human development may not, in some verses at least, go beyond mere embryonic growth to include the transformations of human morphology which took place over the ages : The existence of such changes has been formally proven by paleontology, and the evidence is so overwhelming that it is pointless to question it.

The earliest commentators of the Qur'an could have no inkling of the discoveries that would be made centuries later. They could only view these particular verses in the context of the development of the embryo. There was no alternative at the time.

Then came the Darwinian 'bombshell' which–through the overt twisting of Darwin's theory by his early followers–extrapolated the notion of an evolution that might be applied to man, even though the amplitude of the evolution had not yet been demonstrated in the animals. In Darwin's day, the theory was pushed to extremes, with researchers claiming to have proof that man was descended from the apes–an idea that, even today, no respectable paleontologist is able to demonstrate. There is obviously a very wide gap, however, between the concept of man's descent from the apes (a theory that is totally untenable), and the idea of transformations of the human form in the course of time (which has been fully proven). The confusion between the two reaches its height when they are merged together–with very flimsy arguments–under the banner of the word EVOLUTION. This unfortunate confusion has caused certain people wrongly to imagine that since the word is used in reference to man, it must mean that, *ipso facto,* man's origin may be traced to the apes.

It is crucial to be quite clear about the distinction between the two, otherwise there is a risk of misunderstanding the meaning to be ascribed to certain verses of the Qur'an that I am about to quote. There is not the slightest hint, in these verses, of evidence to support a materialistic theory of the origin of man that justifiably shocks Muslims, Jews and Christians alike.

The Profound Spiritual Meaning of the Creation of Man from the Earth

As the following two verses indicate, man is presented in the Qur'an as a being that is intimately linked with the earth :
–Sura 71, verses 17 and 18 *(Reference nº 1)* :

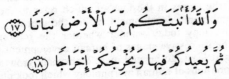

"God has caused you to grow as a growth from the earth, and afterwards, He will make you return there, He will bring you forth again, a [new] forth-bringing."
—Sura 20, verse 55 *(Reference nº 2)*.

The preceding verse mentioned the earth :

مِنْهَا خَلَقْنَكُمْ وَفِيهَا نُعِيدُكُمْ وَمِنْهَا نُخْرِجُكُمْ تَارَةً أُخْرَى

"From [the earth] We [1] fashioned you and into it We shall make you return and from it We shall bring you forth another time."

The spiritual aspect of man's provenance from the earth is emphasized by the fact that we shall return to the earth after death and also by the idea that God will bring us forth again on the Day of Judgement. As we have already seen, the Bible stresses this same spiritual meaning.

With regard to the above translation of Reference nº 2, I should like to point out to my Arabic-speaking and Arabist readers that in the West, the Arabic word *khalaqa* is isually translated by the verb 'to create'. It is important to realize, however, that, as indicated in the excellent dictionary compiled by Kasimirski, the original meaning of the word was 'to give a proportion to a thing, or to make it of a certain proportion or quantity'. For God (alone), the translation has been simplified by the use of the word 'to create', i.e. to bring into existence a thing which did not formerly exist. In so doing, those who exclusively use the term 'to create' refer only to the action; they fail to translate the idea of 'proportion' which accompanies it. A more accurate rendering would perhaps be the verb 'to fashion' or 'to form in due proportion'. This would bring us nearer to the original meaning of the Arabic word. That is why I have opted to use the verb 'to fashion' in most of my translations, with the implied sense of the primitive Arabic meaning.

THE COMPONENTS OF THE GROUND AND THE FORMATION OF MAN

The primary spiritual meaning of man's origin from the ground does not rule out the notion, which is present in the Qur'an, of what we would today call the chemical 'components' of the human body, which are to be found in the ground [2]. In order to convey this

1. 'We' refers to God.
2. By 'components' or 'elements' (terms which are used to make the text easier to read), I am referring to matter which can be extracted from the ground and which does

notion–nowadays acknowledged as scientifically accurate–to the men alive when the Qur'an was revealed, terminology had to be used that was in keeping with the state of knowledge at the time. Man was formed from components contained in the ground. This idea emerges very clearly from numerous verses in which the formative elements are indicated by a variety of names :

–Sura 11, verse 61 *(Reference n° 3)* :

هُوَأَنشَأَكُم مِّنَ ٱلْأَرْضِ

" He [God] caused you to grow from the earth."

The idea of the earth (*arD* in Arabic) is reiterated in sura 53, verse 32.

–Sura 22, verse 5 *(Reference n° 4)*, in which God is speaking to man :

فَإِنَّا خَلَقْنَٰكُم مِّن تُرَابٍ

"We fashioned you from soil."

Man's provenance from soil (*turâb* in Arabic) is repeated in sura 18, verse 37; sura 30, verse 20; sura 35, verse 11 and sura 40, verse 67.

–Sura 6, verse 2 *(Reference n° 5)* :

هُوَ ٱلَّذِى خَلَقَكُم مِّن طِينٍ

"[God] is the One who fashioned you from clay."

Clay (*Tiyn* in Arabic) is used in several verses to define the components from which man was constituted.

–Sura 32, verse 7 *(Reference n° 6)* :

وَبَدَأَ خَلْقَ ٱلْإِنسَٰنِ مِن طِينٍ

not decompose, i.e. the various atomic components which constitute molecules; all the elements which form part of the human body are present in lesser or greater quantities in the ground.

"[God] began the creation of man from clay."

It is important to note at this point that the Qur'an refers to the 'beginning' of a creation from clay: This obviously implies that another stage is to follow.

–Sura 37, verse 11 *(Reference n° 7)*.

Although it does not seem to provide any new data for the present study, the following quotation is given for the sake of completeness. The reference in the verse is to men :

$$ \text{إِنَّا خَلَقْنَـٰهُم مِّن طِينٍ لَّازِبٍ} $$

"We fashioned them from a sticky clay."
–Sura 55, verse 14 *(Reference n° 8)* :

$$ \text{خَلَقَ ٱلْإِنسَـٰنَ مِن صَلْصَـٰلٍ كَٱلْفَخَّارِ} $$

"[God] fashioned man from a clay, like pottery."

The image suggests that man was 'modelled', as indicated in the verse that is to follow. We shall also find the idea of the 'moulding' of man, the subject of the next sub-section.

–Sura 15, verse 26 *(Reference n° 9)* :

$$ \text{وَلَقَدْ خَلَقْنَا ٱلْإِنسَـٰنَ مِن صَلْصَـٰلٍ مِّنْ حَمَإٍ مَّسْنُونٍ} $$

"We have fashioned man from clay, from moulded mud."

The same idea is repeated in sura 15, verses 28-33.

–Sura 23, verse 12 *(Reference n° 10)* :

$$ \text{وَلَقَدْ خَلَقْنَا ٱلْإِنسَـٰنَ مِن سُلَـٰلَةٍ مِّن طِينٍ} $$

"We fashioned man from the quintessence of a clay."

I have used the word 'quintessence' to translate the Arabic term *sulâtat,* which means 'one thing extracted from another thing'. As we shall see later, the word appears in another passage of the Qur'an in which it is stated that man's descent derives from that which is extracted from spermatic liquid; (it is known today that the active component of spermatic liquid is a unicellular organism called a 'spermatozoon').

I imagine that the 'quintessence of a clay' must refer to the various chemical components which constitute clay, extracted from water, which in terms of weight is its main element.

Water, which in the Qur'an is considered to be at the origin of all life, is mentioned as the essential element in the following verse.

–Sura 25, verse 54 *(Reference n° 11) :*

$$\text{وَهُوَ ٱلَّذِى خَلَقَ مِنَ ٱلْمَآءِ بَشَرًا فَجَعَلَهُ نَسَبًا وَصِهْرًا}$$

"[God] is the One who fashioned a man from water and established relationship of lineage [by men] and kinship by women."

As elsewhere in the Qur'an, the 'man' referred to is Adam.

Several verses allude to the creation of woman :

–Sura 4, verse 1 *(Reference n° 12) :*

$$\text{خَلَقَكُمْ مِنْ نَفْسٍ وَاحِدَةٍ وَخَلَقَ مِنْهَا زَوْجَهَا}$$

"[God] is the One who fashioned you from a single person and from that [person] created his wife.".

This verse is repeated in sura 7, verse 189 and sura 39, verse 6. The same subject is referred to in more or less the same terms in sura 30, verse 21 and sura 42, verse 11.

There can be no doubt that in these twelve references, much space is devoted to symbolical reflections on man's origins, including a clear indication of what will happen to him after his death, and containing allusions to the fact that man will return to earth in order to be brought forth again on the Day of Judgement. There would also seem, however, to be a reference to the chemical composition of the human body *(Reference n° 10).*

The Transformations of Man
Over the Ages

In contrast to the above, the commentary suggested by the verses of the Qur'an which I shall quote below bears mainly on material notions. We are indeed in the presence here of genuine morphological transformations which take place in a harmonious and balanced fashion due to an organization that is strictly planned, for the phenomena occur in successive phases. Thus the will of God, who rules eternally over the fate of human communities, is made manifest in all its power and splendour through these events.

The Qur'an first speaks of a 'creation', but it goes on to describe a second stage in which God gave form to man. There can be no doubt that the creation and morphological organization of man are seen as *successive events*.

—Sura 7, verse 11 *(Reference nº 13)*, in which God is speaking to man :

$$\text{وَلَقَدْ خَلَقْنَٰكُمْ ثُمَّ صَوَّرْنَٰكُمْ ثُمَّ قُلْنَا لِلْمَلَٰٓئِكَةِ}$$
$$\text{ٱسْجُدُوا۟ لِءَادَمَ}$$

"We created you and *thereupon* We gave you form; *thereupon,* We told the angels : Bow down to Adam."

Hence it is possible to discern three successive events, the first two of which are important to our study : God created man and *thereupon* gave him a form (*Sawwara,* in Arabic).

Elsewhere, it is stated that man's form will be harmonious :

—Sura 15, verses 28-29 *(Reference nº 14)* :

$$\text{وَإِذْ قَالَ رَبُّكَ لِلْمَلَٰٓئِكَةِ إِنِّى خَٰلِقٌۢ بَشَرًا مِّن صَلْصَٰلٍ}$$
$$\text{مِّنْ حَمَإٍ مَّسْنُونٍ ۝ فَإِذَا سَوَّيْتُهُۥ وَنَفَخْتُ فِيهِ مِن رُّوحِى}$$
$$\text{فَقَعُوا۟ لَهُۥ سَٰجِدِينَ ۝}$$

"When thy Lord said to the angels : I am going to fashion a man from clay, from moulded mud; when I have harmoniously fashioned him and breathed into him of My spirit, fall down, prostrating yourself unto him."

The phrase 'to fashion harmoniously' (*sawway*, in Arabic) is repeated in sura 38, verse 72.

Another verse describes how man's harmonious form is obtained through the presence of equilibrium and complexity of structure (the verb *rakkaba* in Arabic means 'to make a thing from components') :

—Sura 82, verses 7-8 *(Reference nº 15)*:

$$ ٱلَّذِى خَلَقَكَ فَسَوَّىٰكَ فَعَدَلَكَ ۝ $$

$$ فِىٓ أَىِّ صُورَةٍ مَّا شَآءَ رَكَّبَكَ ۝ $$

"[God] is the One who created you, then fashioned you harmoniously and in due proportion; into whatsoever form He willed, He made you out of components."

Man was created *in whatsoever form God willed*. This is an extremely important point :

—Sura 95, verse 4 *(Reference nº 16)*, in which God is speaking :

$$ لَقَدْ خَلَقْنَا ٱلْإِنسَـٰنَ فِىٓ أَحْسَنِ تَقْوِيمٍ $$

"We fashioned man according to the best organizational plan."

The Arabic word *taqwiym* means 'to organize something in a planned way', implying therefore an order of progress that has been strictly defined in advance. It so happens that specialists in evolution, when describing the transformations that occur over the course of time, use that very expression : the organizational plan is surely very evident from scientific studies of the subject.

In sura 95, from which the above verse is taken, the context is the creation of man in general with reference to the fact that once man has thus been given organized form by divine will, he sinks to a wretched condition (implying decrepitude in old age). The sura does not make any mention whatsoever of embryonic development; it simply describes the creation of human beings in general. In terms of structure, the organizational plan obviously refers to the human species as a whole.

–Sura 71, verse 14 *(Reference n° 17)* :

The interpretation I have given to this verse reflects the importance of context as a means of suggesting what a particular word may refer to :

$$\text{وَقَدْ خَلَقَكُمْ أَطْوَارًا}$$

"[God] fashioned you in stages [or phases]."

The Arabic word translated here by 'stages' or 'phases' is *aTwâr* (singular *Tawr*). This is the only verse in the Qur'an in which the word occurs in the plural. It is not possible to search elsewhere in the text to ascertain whether these 'phases' or 'stages'–which quite obviously refer to man–concern man's development in the uterus (which is what the earliest commentators thought, and what I myself supposed to be the case in my previous book), or whether they allude to the transformations that the human species has undergone in the course of time. It is a point worth pondering.

To arrive at an answer, it goes without saying that we must first take account of the subject as described in the Qur'an. Thus we note that sura 71, from which the above verse is taken, deals principally with signs of divine omnipotence and the power of God the Creator in general. The passage in the Qur'an which includes verse 14 (a passage that refers to Noah's sermon to his people) essentially dwells on God's mercy, His generosity in endowing man with His gifts, and His omnipotence in creating man, the heavens, the sun and the moon, and the earth. On the subject of the Creation, the Qur'an mentions the spiritual aspect of the creation of man from the earth *(Reference n° 1,* in the verses quoted above).

At no point whatsoever in sura 71 is there mention of the development of the unborn infant, a feature which traditional commentators of long ago thought was suggested by the word 'phases'. Although the word is not used anywhere else in the text, the Qur'an undoubtedly refers in detail in many other suras to these 'phases' of embryonic development (see next chapter); nevertheless, there is no reference in this particular sura. We cannot, however, rule out the possibility that the passage of the Qur'an here under discussion may indeed have added the development in 'phases' of the embryo in the uterus to the other subjects mentioned above : there is nothing to indicate that it should be excluded.

In fact, the development of the individual and that of the species to which it belongs conforms to the same determining factors over the course of time; those factors are the genes which play a decisive role in the grouping of the paternal and maternal inheritance *at the initial stage of reproduction.* Whether we choose to link these 'phases' with the development of the individual or that of the species, the concept they express remains in perfect harmony with modern scientific data on the subject.

Having said this, the verses preceding Reference n° 17 state sufficiently clearly that the human form undergoes transformations, so that even if we removed Reference n° 17, the general meaning would not be affected.

The following two verses refer to the replacement of one human community by another.

—Sura 76, verse 28 *(Reference n° 18)*, in which God is alluding to men :

نَحْنُ خَلَقْنَاهُمْ وَشَدَدْنَا أَسْرَهُمْ

وَإِذَا شِئْنَا بَدَّلْنَا أَمْثَالَهُمْ تَبْدِيلًا

" Verily, We created them and strengthened all of them. And when We willed, We replaced them completely by people who were of the same kind."

It is highly likely that the 'strengthening' mentioned in the above verse refers to man's physical constitution.

—Sura 6, verse 133 *(Reference n° 19)* :

إِن يَشَأْ يُذْهِبْكُمْ وَيَسْتَخْلِفْ مِنْ بَعْدِكُم مَّا يَشَاءُ

كَمَآ أَنشَأَكُم مِّن ذُرِّيَّةِ قَوْمٍ ءَاخَرِينَ

" If [God] wills, He destroys you and in your place appoints whom He wills as successors, just as He brought you forth from the descendants of other peoples."

These two verses emphasize the disappearance of certain human communities and their replacement by others, according to God's will, during the course of time.

Early commentators have above all seen in these verses a punishment inflicted by God on sinful communities. In general, it was the religious aspect that was primarily stressed. The material fact is there, however, and it is clearly expressed; it consists of the disappearance of various communities (whose size is not mentioned) and the replacement, at a certain period, of a particular human community by the descendants of other peoples.

To sum up, therefore, the human groups that have existed over the course of time may have varied in their morphology, but these modifications have proceeded according to an organizational plan ordained by God; communities disappeared and were replaced by other groups : That, in so many words, is what the Qur'an has to tell us on the subject. It is futile to seek discrepancies between the Qur'an and the data of paleontology, or with the information allowing us to conceive of a creative evolution, for there are none.

Having reached this stage in our examination of the answers provided by the Qur'an to the question 'What is the Origin of Man?' we may perhaps be inclined to think that the subject has been exhausted. After all that have learned from the verses quoted in the preceding two chapters, it would indeed seem so : But let us remember that in the case of one of these verses, we noted how useful it would be to continue our analysis in the light of the data in the Qur'an concerning human reproduction.

In actual fact, the Qur'anic statements dealing with this subject have a bearing on the question of the transformations that have taken place in human morphology over the ages. The latter are indeed governed by the genetic code, formed by the union of chromosomes received from the paternal and maternal reproductive cells. The genetic inheritance thus brought together determines, first in the embryo [1] and then in the foetus [2], the possible appearance of morphological changes as compared with the father and mother. These modifications become definitive after the child is born and during its growth in childhood. At the very least, these modifications provide the child with a structural personality which is unique : Apart from identical twins formed from a single ovule, no one human being is exactly the same as another. At the very most it is a matter of constitutional differences which affect the species itself. It is therefore the combined total of changes that take place over successive generations which ultimately determines the morphological transformations that paleontologists have noted in various human groups from past ages.

1. Before the second month of pregnancy.
2. After the second month of pregnancy.

Consequently, we must review the main points on reproduction contained in the Qur'an. I shall therefore briefly summarize the detailed study of this question that appears in *The Bible, the Qur'an and Science*.

For us to grasp the significance of what is to follow (especially with regard to the comparison between statements contained in the Holy Scriptures and the data of science), we must bear in mind that the text was communicated to man in the seventh century A.D. Any human work composed at that period was bound to set forth inaccurate statements : Science had not yet developed, so it was inevitable that any reference to human reproduction would be riddled with notions culled from myth and superstition. How could it be otherwise, for in order to understand the complex mechanisms involved in this process, man had to possess a knowledge of anatomy and the use of the microscope, and the basic sciences had to be born, paving the way for physiology, embryology and obstetrics?

Reminder of Certain Notions Concerning Human Reproduction

The intention here is not to put forward theories, but to advance ideas based on facts. Theories are by nature open to change; when approached from a theoretical angle, science is always in a state of flux : What is valid today may be disproved tomorrow. A suitable basis for comparison is therefore one which rests on scientific data that are not open to change, having been firmly established and checked through experimentation, and having possibly even been effectively put into practice.

It is an established fact that human reproduction takes place in a sequence of processes, starting with the fertilization, in the Fallopian tube, of an ovule that has detached itself from the ovary half-way throught the menstrual cycle. The fertilizing agent is a cell taken from the male, the spermatozoon, tens of millions of which are contained in a single cubic centimetre of sperm. All that is required to ensure fertilization, however, is a single spermatozoon, in other words, an infinitely small quantity of spermatic liquid. The seminal liquid and the spermatozoa are produced by the testicles and temporarily stored in a system of canals and reservoirs. At the moment of sexual contact, they pass from their place of storage into the urinary tract, and on the way, the liquid is enriched with further secretions that do not, however, contain fertilizing agents. These secretions will nevertheless exercise a considerable influence on fertilization by aiding the sperm to arrive at the point where the female ovule is fertilized. Thus spermatic liquid is a mixture : It contains seminal liquid and various additional secretions.

Once the ovule has been fertilized, it descends into the uterus via the Fallopian tube; even while it is descending, however, it has already begun to divide. Then it literally 'implants' itself by insertion into the thickness of the mucosa and the muscles, once the placenta has been formed.

As soon as the embryo becomes visible to the naked eye, it appears as a very tiny mass of flesh devoid of any distinctive parts. There it develops, gradually acquiring a human shape after stages during which certain parts, such as the head, are considerably larger in volume than the rest of the body; these subsequently reduce, while the basic life-sustaining structures form : the skeleton, surrounded by muscles, the nervous system, the circulatory system, the viscera, etc.

Statements Contained in the Qur'an

The brief summary above outlines the basic stages of development which, in the following pages, we shall compare with the statements contained in the Qur'an. To facilitate comprehension, the points raised in the Qur'an may be listed as follows :
   1) the small volume of liquid required for fertilization;
   2) the complexity of the fertilizing liquid;
   3) the implantation of the fertilized egg;
   4) the evolution of the embryo.

THE SMALL VOLUME OF LIQUID REQUIRED
FOR FERTILIZATION

—Sura 16, verse 4 :

$$\text{خَلَقَ ٱلْإِنسَـٰنَ مِن نُّطْفَةٍ}$$

"[God] fashioned man from a small quantity [of sperm]."
This phrase occurs eleven times in the Qur'an.

The Arabic word translated here as 'a small quantity [of sperm]' is *nuTfat*. This is perhaps not the most ideal rendition, but there does not appear to be any single word in English that quite captures its full meaning. The word comes from the Arabic verb signifying 'to dribble, to trickle'; its primary meaning refers to the trace of liquid left in the bottom of a bucket after the latter has been emptied, in other words a very small quantity of liquid, which is the second meaning of the word : a drop of water. In this particular instance, it is a small quantity of sperm, since the word is associated with the word 'sperm' (*maniyy* in Arabic) in the following verse :

—sura 75, verse 37 :

$$\text{أَلَرْ يَكُ نُطْفَةً مِّن مَّنِيٍّ يُمْنَى}$$

"Was [man] not a small quantity of sperm which has been poured out?"

It is important to realize that the Qur'an states very clearly that the fertilizing capacity of the sperm does not depend on the volume of liquid 'poured out'. The idea that a tiny quantity of liquid is perfectly effective is not immediately obvious. Those ignorant of the real facts concerning these phenomena would tend, indeed, to think the exact opposite. And yet, over one thousand years before the existence of spermatozoa was discovered in the early seventeenth century, the Qur'an expresses ideas that were proven correct, due to the discovery of the identity of the fertilizing agent, measurable in units of $1/1,000$ of a millimetre. It is precisely the spermatozoon, present in the seminal liquid, that contains the D.N.A. tape; this in turn forms the vehicle for the genes provided by the father, which unite with the genes from the mother to form the genetic inheritance of the future individual.

The genes contained in the male reproductive cell constitute—in conjunction with those of the female reproductive cell—the factors which are to determine the many characteristics of the future human being. As we have seen earlier in this book, once chromatic reduction has taken place, the spermatozoa are carriers of genes that contain factors which dictate that the individual is to be either a male (hemichromosome Y) or female (hemichromosome X). If, of the innumerable spermatozoa that cluster around the edge of the ovule as possible fertilizing cells, the one which actually succeeds in fertilizing it contains a Y hemichromosome, the future child will be a boy ; if the spermatozoon that penetrates the ovule contains an X hemichromosome, the child will be a girl. The individual's sex is therefore genetically determined at the actual moment of fertilization by the fertilizing agent, in an infinitely small volume, and thereafter, the child's sexual characteristics remain set. The Qur'an contains the following statement on the subject (the reference is to man) :

—sura 80, verse 19 :

$$ مِن نُّطْفَةٍ خَلَقَهُ فَقَدَّرَهُ $$

"From a small quantity of liquid, [God] fashioned him [in due proportion] and ordained his fate."

(I have translated the world *Khalaqa* according to its original meaning—mentioned in the preceding chapter—which is 'to fashion in due proportion' or 'to form', in preference to the verb 'to create'.)

We must surely admit that there is in this instance a striking conformity between the statements in the Qur'an concerning a fate *ordained at this stage* and our knowledge of the fact that it is the genetic inheritance received from the father which determines the sex of the individual—a point that was emphasized above.

THE COMPLEXITY OF THE FERTILIZING LIQUID

This is a very precise concept, and it is clearly expressed in the following verse of the Qur'an :

—sura 76, verse 2, in which God is speaking :

$$ إِنَّا خَلَقْنَا الْإِنسَانَ مِن نُّطْفَةٍ أَمْشَاجٍ $$

"Verily, We fashioned man from a small quantity of mingled liquids."

The term 'mingled liquids' corresponds to the Arabic word *amchâj*. Early commentators took this word to mean a male and a female liquid [1], just as if the female produced liquids that performed a role in reproduction : This interpretation is untenable. It is simply a reflection of the ideas current at the time the Qur'an was communicated to man, a period in which, quite naturally nothing was known of female physiology or embryology. This explains why early commentators believed in the existence of a liquid originating from the female which took part in the process of fertilization. Opinions such as these, which are expressed by commentators who

---

1. If this were the case, the laws of grammar—an aspect of the Qur'anic text that is never at fault—would dictate that the word appear in the dual form, and not in the plural as it appears here.

are undoubtedly most eminently qualified to speak of religious questions, unfortunately continue to exercice an influence on the interpretations given by today's experts concerning subjects of a different kind, namely the natural phenomena. We must therefore insist on the fact that the ovule from the female is not contained in a liquid such as sperm, and that the various secretions which do occur in the vagina and the uterine mucosa have absolutely nothing to do with the formation of a new individual as far as their actual substance is concerned.

The 'mingled liquids' to which the Qur'an refers are specific to spermatic liquid whose complexity is thus suggested.

As we know, this liquid is composed of secretions from the following glands : the testicles, the seminal vesicles, the prostate and the glands annexed to the urinary tract.

This is not all the Qur'an mentions : It also informs us that the male fertilizing agent is taken from spermatic liquid :
—sura 32, verse 8 :

ثُمَّ جَعَلَ نَسْلَهُ مِن سُلَالَةٍ مِّن مَّآءٍ مَّهِينٍ

"[God] made his progeny from the quintessence of a despised liquid."

The adjective 'despised' (*mahiyn* in Arabic) should be applied not so much to the nature of the liquid itself, as to the fact that it is emitted through the outlet of the urinary tract by way of the canal used for passing urine.

As for the word 'quintessence', we are again in the presence of the Arabic word *sulâlat*, to which we referred earlier in the discussion of the formation of man, during the Creation, from the 'quintessence' of clay. It alludes to a 'thing that is extracted from another thing', as we noted above, and also to the 'best part of a thing'. The concept expressed here inevitably makes us think of spermatozoon.

THE IMPLANTATION OF THE EGG
IN THE FEMALE GENITAL ORGANS

The implantation of the fertilized ovule in the uterus is mentioned in numerous verses of the Qur'an. The Arabic word used in this context is *ealaq*, the exact meaning of which is 'something which clings', as in the following verses :

—sura 75, verses 37 and 38:

$$ اَلَمْ يَكُ نُطْفَةً مِّن مَّنِيٍّ يُمْنَى ۝ $$

$$ ثُمَّ كَانَ عَلَقَةً فَخَلَقَ فَسَوَّى ۝ $$

"Was [man] not a small quantity of sperm which has been poured out? After that, he was something which clings; then God fashioned him in due proportion and harmoniously."

It is an established fact that the fertilized ovule is implanted in the uterine mucosa on roughly the sixth day following fertilization, and anatomically speaking, the egg is indeed something which *clings*.

The idea of 'clinging' expresses the original meaning of the Arabic word *ealaq*. One of the derived meanings of the term is 'blood clot', an interpretation which we still find in today's translations of the Qur'an. This totally inaccurate rendition was first given by commentators of long ago who invented their interpretation according to the derived sense of the word. For lack of knowledge at the time, they had no way of realizing that the original meaning of the word was perfectly adequate. Besides, when it comes to verses which have a bearing on modern knowledge, there is a general rule which has never been found wrong: The oldest, most primitive meaning of a word is always the one which most clearly suggests a comparison with scientific discoveries, while derived meanings invariably lead to statements that are either inaccurate or just plain nonsensical.

THE EVOLUTION OF THE EMBRYO
INSIDE THE UTERUS

Once it has evolved beyond the stage characterized in the Qur'an by the simple word 'something which clings', the embryo, so the Qur'an tells us, goes through a phase in which it literally looks like flesh (chewed flesh). As we know, it preserves this appearance until roughly the twentieth day, when it then begins gradually to take on a human form. Osseous tissue and the bones appear in the embryo, which are subsequently enveloped by the muscles. The idea is expressed in the Qur'an as follows:

–sura 23, verse 14, in which God is speaking :

$$ثُمَّ خَلَقْنَا النُّطْفَةَ عَلَقَةً فَخَلَقْنَا الْعَلَقَةَ مُضْغَةً
فَخَلَقْنَا الْمُضْغَةَ عِظَامًا فَكَسَوْنَا الْعِظَامَ لَحْمًا$$

"We fashioned the thing which clings into a lump of chewed flesh and We fashioned the chewed flesh into bones and We clothed the bones with intact flesh."

The two types of flesh are given different names in the Qur'an : The first–'chewed flesh'–is called *muDḡat,* while the second–'intact flesh'–is designated by the word *laHm* which indeed describes very accurately what muscle actually looks like.

The Qur'an also mentions the emergence of the senses and the viscera :

–sura 32, verse 9 :

$$وَجَعَلَ لَكُمُ السَّمْعَ وَالْأَبْصَارَ وَالْأَفْئِدَةَ$$

"[God] appointed for you the sense of hearing, sight and the viscera."

The allusion in the Qur'an to the sexual organs must also be recalled, for the reference is particularly precise, as the following verses show :

–sura 53, verses 45 and 46 :

$$وَأَنَّهُ خَلَقَ الزَّوْجَيْنِ الذَّكَرَ وَالْأُنْثَى ۝
مِنْ نُطْفَةٍ إِذَا تُمْنَى ۝$$

"[God] fashioned the two of a pair, the male and the female, from a small quantity [of sperm] when it is poured out."

As we have seen above, the Qur'an stresses the fact that only a very small quantity of spermatic liquid is required for fertilization.

The male fertilizing agent, the spermatozoon, contains the hemi-chromosome that is to determine the sex of the future individual : The decisive moment occurs when the spermatozoon penetrates the ovule, and thereafter the sex does not change. The verses quoted above state that the sex of the individual is determined by the small quantity of fertilizing liquid. It is this liquid which carries the sperma-tozoon containing the hemichromosome that determines the sexual features of the new human being. In this context, the text of the Qur'an and the data of modern embryology are strikingly similar.

All these statements agree with today's firmly established facts. But how could the men living at the time of Muhammad have known so many details of embryology? For these data were not discovered until a thousand years after the Qur'anic Revelation had taken place. The history of science leads us to conclude that there can be no human explanation for the existence of these verses in the Qur'an.

The Transformations of the Human Form Over the Ages and Embryonic Development

For those who are unfamiliar with embryology and genetics, it is not immediately obvious that each and every modification which takes place within the individual proceeds from changes that occur in the genes given to the new individual by the chromosomes inherited from its father and mother. As stated earlier, a division takes place in each genetic inheritance which is followed by a unification of elements taken from each half. This quickly results in the beginnings of morphological changes during pregnancy, and hence of functional modifications which appear later on; thus transformations are continued after the birth of the infant, lasting through childhood growth, until the individual reaches adulthood and the transformations are fully completed.

Unless these concepts are properly understood, errors may occur in the ideas of those who are accustomed to thinking that the verses from the Qur'an quoted in this chapter concern only the develop-ment of the infant in the uterus, to the exclusion of the individual's subsequent morphological development. That is why it is crucial to include all the verses that refer to human reproduction in our study of the parts of the Qur'anic text which—as far as I can see—deal with the transformations of the human form over the ages.

To clarify the issue, I shall give an example concerning a pathological transformation consisting of a congenital deficiency that is particularly common among human malformations : The case in question is mongolism. Discoveries have shown that it is caused by the trebling of a chromosome that has been given the number 21, from which the deficiency derives the name 'trisomy 21.' It is today known that the cause lies in genes contained in this chromosome, and that the deficiency occurs with maximum frequency when the mother of the infant is over forty years old.

The disease is characterized by an infantile physical development and intelligence, and certain specific morphological features which may not be very pronounced at birth, but later become very obvious. Thus the condition is recognized more or less early according to its degree of seriousness. Whatever the case, however, its basic characteristics are acquired during the first few weeks of life.

Morphological modifications of a different kind in humans follow the same pattern. The process begins during pregnancy and gradually becomes more and more pronounced until the individual reaches adulthood. Thus, over the successive generations separating the Australopithecus from modern man (which fall into units of 10,000), it is reasonable to suppose that slight modifications took place in each generation, which gradually accumulated until they produced transformations that gave birth to man as we know him today.

It is therefore impossible, as far as the final result is concerned, to separate the slight, concordant modifications that took place with each generation in the uterus from the overall transformations that occurred over a large number of generations. This explanation is necessary to an understanding of the way in which the concept is expressed in the Qur'an, in reference to the evolution of the embryo in the uterus, according to God's will, as stated quite clearly in the Qur'an.

V

THE COMPATIBILITY BETWEEN RELIGION AND SCIENCE

THE MANY APPROACHES TO THE QUESTION

Among the many questions posed by the meaning of our earthly existence, two important points are invariably raised : What is our ultimate destiny and what is the origin of the human species, to which we belong? In the case of the first question, secular knowledge seems to suggest that we are gradually moving toward annihilation [1]. In the case of the second point, as we have already seen, modern knowledge has enabled us to refer to strictly material facts that play an important part in our study of the origin of man.

To what extent is this an advantage or a disadvantage? Some thinkers will say that there is a benefit to be derived from the inclusion of secular data in the analysis of the problem, while others will express the opposite. One wonders whether, over the course of time, it has been both a disadvantage to a sound idea, and then later on, a helpful addition. According to people's religious beliefs, the responses to the question are radically different. Nevertheless, everybody would like to understand : In their research, some thinkers lay heavy emphasis on the ideas to be found in the Scriptures, while others rely on the data supplied by secular

---

1. As far as the purely physical destiny of the human body is concerned, there can be no doubt that the state of 'dust' (or its equivalent), to which the Scriptures of the monotheistic religions tell us we shall be reduced, indeed corresponds to the future indicated by secular knowledge. Moreover, the predictions of science affect subjects that go beyond the scope of our own planet. This is the case for the solar system, in other words the sun and its satellites, one of which is the earth. From a physical point of view, it is possible to predict, at the extreme limit, a process that would result in a 'reduction' of matter. This process would cause our remains to become even more minute. Before this final stage, however, the earth–containing our remains–would have become a lifeless celestial body, just like the moon. As for the Holy Scriptures, they embody the promise that we shall be brought to life again, and raised up from the ground to be presented at the Last Judgement.

knowledge. Surely a more balanced approach today would be to take account of both sources of information, for they do not appear to be in opposition, as was once suggested.

Leaving aside the case of those who systematically and automatically reject the idea of God, the answer to the question, "What is the Origin of Man?", will undoubtedly depend to a great extent, not only on the strength of the faith that people possess, but also on their degree of knowledge in the fields included in the study. In spite of what people may think, such knowledge is not always to the detriment of spiritual values.

In modern times, a scientific background may indeed contribute reasons that, far from causing people to reject the idea of God, may in fact bring them nearer to it by inducing man to reflect on certain discoveries that science has allowed us to make. Within the context of this present study, it is first and foremost the prodigious organization and perpetuation of life that leads us to acknowledge, not only as possible, but as *highly likely* that there exists a Creator. Conversely, the absence of a scientific background does not help those inclined to accept ideas that negate God's existence to understand certain evident facts—as described in the preceding chapters—that speak very clearly in favour of His existence.

This is how credance has been given to certain materialistic theories by those who prefer abstractions or pure metaphysics to the realities of nature as revealed by science. The very attempt to interest such people in material facts is doomed to failure, for science is completely alien to them; in their opinion, science should yield to their abstract constructions, for these, and these alone, have provided them with the immediate answer, and for them, that answer is definitive.

Another approach to the subject is to say that the highly advanced study of the phenomena of life at the cellular level—such as we have seen in the last few decades in the fields of molecular biology and genetics— may cause the scientist to think that there is good reason to continue in this area, progressing at the same breakneck speed and perhaps dispelling the present mystery surrounding the beginnings of life. It is difficult not to be struck today by the fact that certain thinkers, who until now have approached the problem from a strictly materialistic point of view, are beginning to realize that the question must henceforth be seen in a light that introduces—at the very least—certain metaphysical considerations. For example, shortly before his death, the biologist Jean Rostand was asked a question concerning God during one of this talks on French television : Jean Rostand's reply was that, until then, he had not believed in the existence of God, but as a biologist, he admitted that he was at a loss for words when he contemplated the activity that took place at the level of the infinitely small.

In more general terms, we must surely realize that science does not simply have the effect of spreading boundless enthusiasm for unlimited possibilities of discovery in the future. It also causes us to stop and question the disregard for religious teachings that it has undoubtedly provoked in the minds of many people in the West. This leads us, therefore, to try and gain a closer grasp of the question—a perennial theme since the mineteenth century—of the opposition between the teachings of science and religion. In this context, the origin of man is surely a subject that gives rise to numerous reflections.

For many years, it has seemed to me that the problem ought to be approached from the points of view of the three monotheistic religions by asking the following question: How could Jews, Christians and Muslims all accept both the teachings specific to each of the three religions and the data of secular knowledge on the origins of man? Can a person who believes in God find a compatibility between his religious ideas and the discoveries of science in this field? There is only one way of approaching the subject: We must render as accurate an account as possible of the established data of scientific knowledge, and then proceed to an unbiased, logical comparison with the teachings of the Scriptures possessed by each of the three religions. This is what I have attempted to do. The time has now come to give a general survey of the results that arise from this comparison.

THE DIFFICULTIES ENCOUNTERED

The examination of the arguments put forward in the second half of the nineteenth century, following the first edition of Darwin's work in 1859, showed that as far as man's origins were concerned, people in Darwin's day reasoned more by analogy with ideas suggested– rather lightly at the time–on the subject of the animal kingdom, than by a process of highly disciplined deduction. Moreover, the controversy gave rise more to passionate arguments than to scientific comparisons, documented with firm evidence and worthy of serious consideration. Furthermore, the idea of natural selection, which was constantly put forward, was surely nothing but an extrapolation that extended to the power of nature factors which man, through artificial selection, had shown to be suitable for the modification of certain features of a definite species and unsuitable for the profound modification of animal structures. In vaunting these supposed 'virtues' of natural selection, people were far more interested in mere words or wishful thinking than in sound logic, and they defended what was no more than an ideology, based on flimsy scientific data.

The problem has today become extremely complex, owing to the considerable increase in our knowledge, and should therefore be dealt with in two stages. First, we should consider the matter in hand, in other words the facts such as they may be established with the help of material data. Next, we should look for explanations. For these to be valid, however, they must be directly related to the facts themselves, and not to the personal views of those who discovered them.

We have already seen, however, the extent to which certain researchers have deviated from duly proven facts. What is meant here are the firmly established data of paleontology based on the examination of fossils, and not the imaginative reconstructions described earlier in this book. The latter resulted in the presentation of 'models' of prehistoric men based on a few fragments of cranium or other scanty vestiges of skeleton. Those who are not well-versed in the subject are misled into believing that far more is known about it than the documentary evidence–in reality very slim–would tend to indicate.

Over and above this, certain researchers invariably proceed by analogy with events that may have taken place in the animal kingdom at infinitely earlier periods. It has been suggested that if the history of the world were reduced to twenty-four hours, today's man would have appeared in a fraction of the last minute. The major events in the evolution of the animal kingdom came to an end tens of millions of years ago. The last important transformations in the human species took place tens of thousands of years ago. These figures are significant, even if they merely indicate the size of the time-scale, which is the only notion to be noted in this context.

The chronology of events, the progress toward complexity, the halt in the phenomena–all the concepts to which paleontology, zoology, botany and embryology have contributed–are fundamental notions. Considerable erudition is required to grasp them all in detail, and very few people possess such wide-ranging knowledge. There are too many brilliant researchers who choose to ignore them.

It appears, however, that as a result of studies in molecular biology and genetics, the data discovered in the area concerning the organization of cellular life provide new insights into the course of events that led to fully developed human beings. As we have seen, the concept of creative evolution allowed us to grasp the process (which it incorporates) of the course of that evolution. In contrast, other concepts pay little heed to facts which still need to be explained, and therefore lack credibility : The theory of chance and necessity is an exemple of this.

In the same vein, theories have been constructed which are a reflection of the metaphysical system of those who put them forward, rather than the result of observed reality. Thus researchers have managed to formulate concepts that completely miss the point as far as man is concerned. Moreover, when scientists claim to rely on such changing data as those supplied by psychology, thus hoping to find common features between man and animals (from which they draw analogies that lead them to concepts suggesting biological kinship), confusion reigns supreme.

An added difficulty lies in the opinions that one reads or hears in various quarters concerning the contents of the Holy Scriptures; this applies to the Bible and the Qur'an alike. Statements are often attributed to one or other of the texts which do not in fact appear in either of them. When it is claimed that a certain statement in the Scripture has been proven by science–although this is not the case at all–the credibility of the text is even more seriously undermined. As far as the Bible is concerned, on the main points, we are fortunately able to rely on extremely respectable texts, such as the 'Traduction Œcuménique' [*Ecumenical Translation*] in French, the Revised Standard Version in English, or the various translations published by the Biblical School of Jerusalem. In the case of the Qur'an, translations are essential, for five-sixths of the Muslim world do not read Arabic. Unfortunately, mistranslations abound in these texts whenever they touch on subjects that lend themselves to scientific investigation : This is particularly apparent in statements on man. The habit of translating texts in the light of the interpretations suggested by early commentators–whose view of reality could not possibly be in keeping with today's discoveries–plays an important part in the misunderstanding of the Scriptures. I should like to warn the reader against the discrepancy that exists between the translations of the verses quoted in the present work, and the translations he will find in the texts currently in use : As far as the subject in hand is concerned, the latter are riddled with errors.

THE CONCEPT OF CREATION AND SCIENCE

The monotheistic religions do not acknowledge any explanation of man's presence on earth other than that he was created by God. We find this stated in the two Old Testament narratives and also in the Qur'an. While science does not provide any formal proof to support this theory, nor does it suggest any arguments that speak against it or which lead us to regard it as a legend to be abandoned. The concept of evolution in the animal kingdom (which cannot be denied today) would not be changed at all if God, in His omnipotence, had decided at a particular point to allow a new pair of living beings to appear on earth. These new beings would obviously have had to possess anatomical features and functional capacities similar to those of other beings, living in identical or similar surroundings and, like all other beings, adapted to that environment : This accounts for the more or less close resemblance of their structures. Once this new pair had been created, they could have formed the origin of a human lineage which, over the course of millions of years, underwent the physical transformations that the data of paleontology undeniably indicate. Thus, as the Qur'an seems to suggest, the man created by God may well have evolved with regard to his form. The text of the Qur'an also mentions the disappearance of human communities, which were subsequently replaced by members of other communities bearing morphological features that resembled those of their forebears. Today's human type could indeed be the result of these phenomena and events.

The above approach to our origins could be said to reconcile the general principle of the creation of man by God, according to the form He willed, with all the organizational improvements that have appeared in the course of time in living beings; in this context, the lineage of the primates, with the great apes at the top, provides the most fully developed types in the animal kingdom. Thus one can argue that man was created with a morphology that is similar to that of the group mentioned above. When the naturalists closely examine the case of man and that of the animals which are structurally most similar to him, they develop comparisons which rest on logical bases. As far as morphology and certain functions were concerned, the resemblances between man and the great apes–which cannot be denied–were imposed on man, who of necessity was obliged to live in the same surroundings (taking the word in its broadest sense to mean our earthly environment, with its geographical variations.) Thus, man needed a respiratory tract, similar to that of other animals which consume the oxygen in the air, and a digestive tract to ensure his nutrition from the food provided by the earth or the flesh of other animals on which man depends, just like those animals themselves. One could continue the list of other characteristics of human organization, but the resulting conclusions would be the same, for without these morphological and functional resemblances, man could not survive on earth. Certain scientists, paleontologists and specialists from other disciplines are therefore abusing their authority when they invoke these similarities to defend the theory that man is descended from the lineage of the great apes, *for they do not possess one iota of evidence to prove their theory.*

Having said this however, we cannot rule out the possibility that, in one or several related but independent lineages of hominids, fully developed human groups may have appeared owing to certain genetic modifications arising from God's creative genius. A creation of this kind cannot be proven, but it is perfectly logical and does not provoke any objections from the point of view of either paleontology or the natural sciences. The above hypothesis causes those who are aware of the latest discoveries in cellular functions–such as the control of those functions by the genetic code–to weigh the matter very seriously. The scientific point raised here is suggested by our knowledge of the role of genetic inheritance in living beings over the course of time, and by our discovery of the fantastic organizational complexity of the tiniest living forms, ranging from the most rudimentary to the most complex organisms.

Creative evolution may thus be said to have caused the appearance of a human lineage which was subsequently to undergo its own specific transformations. The latter took place within an organizational pattern that manifested itself at various levels over the course of time. The growing complexity of structures, as mentioned above, came from the gradual accumulation of new information concerning the development of anatomical formations and functions, above all regarding the brain.

The foregoing is obviously nothing but a hypothesis, for there is no scientific argument to indicate that the creative power of God manifested itself in such conditions : No fossilized remains have ever been discovered which might prove it. The hypothesis cannot therefore be said to rest on any formal scientific evidence : Today's knowledge simply indicates that we should not consider it impossible that man's appearance occured in this way. I should even go so far as to say that if formal evidence were one day discovered that connected man to an animal ancestry–not that there is the remotest likelihood of this happening–, and if God in His omnipotence had created new information to endow the lineage with human features containing the same possibilities of evolution toward fully developed man, all of these events would to me seem equally compatible with the data mentioned in the present book.

If we argued in the opposite direction, we might state that the creation of the human species took place independently of any pre-existing lineage and that it subsequently underwent the trans-formations described earlier : Not the slightest objection could be raised to this hypothesis, however, as far as the Qur'anic Revelation is concerned.

Whatever theory one puts forward, the general concept of the Creation as stated by the Scriptures of the monotheistic religions does not seem to be in any way incompatible with the data supplied by science.

EVOLUTION IN THE ANIMAL KINGDOM AND THE TRANSFORMATIONS OF THE HUMAN FORM

As we saw in the preceding chapter, the general concept of the Creation embodied in the Holy Scriptures does not stand in opposition to scientific data. Let us now decide whether there is a contradiction between, on the one hand, the phenomena of evolution in the animal kingdom and the transformations in the human form over the ages, and on the other hand, the teachings of the Holy Scriptures.

It will be noted that in this context, I am dealing only with data that have been firmly established by modern knowledge : the fact that there is an evolution in the animal kingdom, and that the human form long ago underwent transformations. The question of relationships or kinship between the animal kingdom and the human lineage will not be broached here, for it was raised earlier with regard to the many gaps that exist in our knowlegde. As we have seen, it is extremely easy for some researchers to consider as proven fact what is at the very most a hypothesis that is not without logic. It is indeed quite interesting to hear eminent scientists making such suggestions, but one cannot accept them as indisputable data which would then be convincing. In order to respect data that are well-founded, and thereby to avoid being misled by mere hypothesis, the case of the animal kingdom and that of man must each be examined separately.

There can be no doubt that evolution exists in the animal kingdom. This is indicated by the appearance of the main phyla, in which features become perfectly distinctive and are present in the entire lineage; divisions occur, in which new characteristics are individualized. Within the groups thus formed, subdivisions appear which can be broken down into classes, orders, families, and so on, each of which presents specific features that add new characterictics to each subdivision. The evolution of these various groups progresses in different phases : starting, accelerating, decelerating and stopping. Certain groups persistently survive throughout the course of time, while others eventually disappear. All of these facts are proven beyond a shadow of a doubt, and nobody questions them. What is open to discussion is the determination of these phenomena. The methods by which the phenomena become a reality are suggested by studies of the cell, and in particular the genes.

There is no reference in the Qur'an to evolution in the animal kingdom. In contrast, the Bible provides the Sacerdotal versions of Genesis, in which we find the creation of the animals 'each according to its kind'. By using this expression, the Bible indicates that the animals were created in the manner imagined by the men who lived at the time the Biblical texts were written. According to the Bible, therefore, the animals have not changed during the period that separates the time the text was written from the discoveries of modern science. As far as this point is concerned, the Biblical authors expressed themselves in the language of their day.

In contrast, there is every reason to believe that the transforma- tions of the human form that took place over the ages are referred to in the Qur'an. The references which appear in the passages quoted earlier indeed seem to allude to changes that affected the entire human species after man had appeared on earth, thus going far beyond mere statements on the development of the fertilized ovule in the uterus that results in a new human being : The transformations in the uterus are mentioned in the Qur'an, as we have already seen in the chapter entitled 'Human Reproduction.'

The morphological changes that have occurred in man over the ages must be seen in the light of the data supplied by genetics. The long-term transformations of man could only have been produced by a series of 'reshapings' that occurred over successive generations, gradually accumulating in the course of time under the influence of new information supplied by the genetic inheritance. The process began at the embryonic and foetal stage, and the action of new information [1] continued after birth and throughout childhood; it particularly affected human structures, For example, a feature that has changed considerably over the course of time is the cranial capacity, which, in conjunction with the development of the brain, has increased considerably. These changes have required constant and successive modifications over a very large number of genera-

1. Recorded on the D.N.A. tape.

tions, for each transformation has been very small indeed. They have all taken place in an ordered fashion under the control of the genetic inheritance, and *each modification has begun at the embryonic stage*. Without a change occuring in the uterus, at the level of the cells and the as yet undifferentiated tissues, genuine transformations cannot take place : After a certain stage of evolution, the cells and differentiated tissues are 'locked' on a certain course which determines their future. For example, once the individual has been born, the organism cannot produce a new organization of the nervous system, conditioned by the increase in the brain's functional complexity : The outline and development of its growth can only occur before birth.

In view of the above, all the events that take place within the uterus have a direct bearing on the series of modifications that appear over the course of time : The latter are simply the practical result of the accumulations of the former.

Obviously, however, these notions can only be understood if one is aware of the influence exercised by the genetic code on intra-uterine development. It is my profound conviction that one cannot fully grasp the meaning of certain verses in the Qur'an concerning man, unless one possesses a knowledge of the data on this subject discovered in recent decades. If one compares the statements in the Qur'an with the findings of genetics, however, the true meaning of the verses becomes perfectly clear. Needless to say, the verses were intelligible to man throughout the ages, but until recently, commentators have only been able to uncover their apparent meaning. Men in days gone by were perfectly satisfied with this, however, for through their own interpretation of the verses, they perceived the basic purpose of the Book : to help man understand God's omnipotence, the prime task of any Holy Scripture. Additional aid is now supplied by science through the discovery of the true meaning of the Qur'anic text, which at the same time shows the complete concordance between the two.

In view of this, we are unable to find contradictions between the statements in the Qur'an on human transformations over the ages and the firmly established data of paleontology concerning extremely early human forms whose features differ in certain respects from those of present-day man. We should bear in mind the facts already mentioned concerning the fossilized human forms dating from several million years ago (the Australopithecus), less ancient forms (such as Neanderthal Man, who most likely lived some 100,000 years ago), and more recent forms (such as Cro-Magnon Man), from which, in practical terms, our own species evolved

(Homo Sapiens, which appeared some 40,000 years ago.) Let me once again stress, however, that there are gaps in our knowledge, caused by the lack of human vestiges. They affect periods that may be counted in millions, hundreds of thousands, or tens of thousands of years, depending on the case in question. A possible explanation for these gaps is the fact that the human population of the world was very small in those prehistoric times : A comparison of human and animal remains discovered in terranes dating from the same period indicates the rarity of human vestiges. Nevertheless, the remains that have been found and acknowledged today as such are indeed human. This is borne out by the discovery of traces of human industry, which, while admittedly rudimentary, are undoubtedly the product of beings that displayed an intelligence and a capacity for fashioning implements.

We now possess incontrovertible evidence indicating that present-day man is not quite the same as the human forms that lived long ago, whose remains we have recently discovered; the existence of transformations within the human species over the course of time is therefore undeniable, and is as obvious as the fact that the earth is round. While the Bible does not specifically mention these changes, the Qur'an tells us that they occured after man was created : The Holy Scripture is therefore in perfect agreement with scientific data on this point.

CELLULAR ORGANIZATION
AND THE ORIGIN OF THE GENETIC CODE:
A SCIENTIFIC ENIGMA

While we know that cellular organization functions according to the genetic code, the origin of this 'command system' remains an enigma.

J. Monod, who vigorously defended the role of chance and neccessity, which he considered to be determinant, was therefore obliged to make the following admission, already quoted from the book he published in 1970 : "The major problem is the origin of the genetic code and the mechanism by which it is expressed. Indeed, one cannot talk so much of a 'problem' as of a genuine enigma." It is a pity that the famous molecular biologist, although aware of the existence of this enigma, chose chance as the unique power to fill this gap in our knowledge. It is indeed a very serious deficiency, for, without wishing to go into detail again, it must be remembered that the intimate functioning of the cell is governed by a 'central control', located within the nucleus, which regulates the information recorded in the genes.

The genes govern the chemical activity within the cell which results in exchanges of matter and energy according to a precise ' code. They rely on 'messengers' adapted to each task and also to reproduction. In the case of the unicellular beings which are even more simple, for they do not contain a nucleus, (such as the bacteria), the D.N.A. tape is in direct contact with the cytoplasm. Activity of this kind is quite considerable, especially with regard to the reproduction of bacteria. Indeed, a new bacteria can be formed from the substance of the bacteria itself within the space of twenty minutes, following the information received from the genes recorded on the D.N.A. tape. During each division, the tape is duplicated in its entirety within the new organism : This is how life is passed on. The chemical functions of the bacteria are in fact extremely numerous : Escherichia Coli can produce three thousand species of protein. The D.N.A. tape of this bacteria, on which the genes are recorded, is said to be one millimetre long (roughly 5,000 times its length at the longest point, which is already quite considerable.)

In the case of a human cell, the D.N.A. tape is 1,000 times longer. The system is far more complex, however, than this figure would suggest, for while the bacteria is composed of a single living element, man is made up of an enormous number of cells. Their functions are coordinated by a multitude of regulatory systems, affecting all of man's constitutive elements. When taken together, the human cells possess a D.N.A. tape, on which man's genes are recorded, which is roughly equal in length to the distance from the earth to the sun. For every human individual, this represents a colossal mass of information. As mentioned earlier in this book, the single human cell contains a host of data which are expressed in molecular terms by the genes located on roughly one metre of D.N.A. tape for each cell.

We are therefore confronted with two questions :

1) How could the simplest organization (or almost the simplest, as far as the bacteria are concerned) supply such an enormous mass of information, regulating each and every function, including reproduction? This raises the question of the origin of the genetic code in the rudimentary beings.

2) How could the genetic code, ranging from the bacteria to man, have become so enriched with new information? For by giving rise to a new living organism, thus introducing a modification in comparison with the being that preceded it, the genetic code must necessarily have already possessed the new information required by the reproductive cells in order to engender an individual displaying slight dissimilarities compared with the one preceding it. It is obviously very difficult to imagine that the simplest living organism could possess all the genes that subsequently came to be distributed throughout the various species of animal : Evolution in the animal kingdom must have taken place with the creation of new genes.

The latter regulate functions that grow increasingly complex as one rises in the animal scale. They guide the anatomical and functional organization of all the living beings.

The constitution of an initial genetic code for the most primitive beings remains a scientific enigma. So does the enrichment of that code through the introduction of new genes, a process that is crucial to the most evolved species, involving ever-larger numbers of genes as one ascends the animal scale. The failure of science to provide an answer to the above enigmas shifts the emphasis of our study from the material to the metaphysical.

In this context, those who believe in God are more than willing to suggest the intervention of His creative genius : Science itself has shown that the theory of a creative influence, operating in the strict order present in evolution, is in perfect agreement with material findings.

The questions which any thinking person is likely to ask about the origins of the staggeringly complex organization of the cell find their answer in these very same scientific discoveries. Molecular biology has shown the infinite variety of chemical functions to be found within a single cell, all of them operating in perfect coordination, and has indicated the prodigious capacity for the production of proteins possessed by the human cell. Through the genetic information it contains, the nucleus controls all of these functions.

Once again, we are confronted with the same enigma ; it raises the same questions and these in turn suggest the same replies.

THE EVOLUTION OF LIVING BEINGS, A SPECIAL CASE WITHIN THE GENERAL EVOLUTION OF THE UNIVERSE

In spite of the inaccuracies specific to certain Scriptures, the causes of which we have already examined, the monotheistic religions all present a view of the world that stands in sharp contrast to the metaphysical concepts put forward by the thinkers of Antiquity, among them the Greek philosophers.

The Yahvist version of Genesis was written in the ninth or tenth century B.C. Although the Biblical authors wrote in the language of their day, their narration of the Creation is nevertheless a work of inspiration which expresses certain general ideas concerning the universe. These notions were put forward long before the works of the eminent Greek philosophers, and yet they are infinitely more accurate than the latter, for by and large, they are corroborated by modern science. Empedocles, Plato and, for that matter, Aristotle, as well as many others, considered that the universe had neither a beginning nor an end, and that everything existed throughout eternity.

In writing the Sacerdotal version of the Bible, in the sixth century B.C., the priests at the Temple of Jesuralem adapted to their own purposes the primitive concept of a creation, embroidering their narrative with details which later proved to be utterly fictitious.

Christianity bases its concept of the origin of man on the information contained in the Old Testament. Moreover, it emphasizes the end of time and the Last Judgement that is to come after the Resurrection of the dead.

The Qur'an was communicated to man in the seventh century A.D. It refers to the creation of the world, man's appearance on earth, the end of the created world, and the destiny of man in the life to come, following the Resurrection of the dead and the Last Judgement. The Qur'an does not, however, contain the inaccuracies that are to be found in the Bible. It provides precise information on certain points that, in the West, come as a great surprise for many people today. We shall return to these in a moment. Modern science has taught us that the earth, the stars and the planets all have a definite age, and that they have all evolved over the course of time. It is of course difficult to provide a precise figure for the date of the formation of the universe : Some scientists estimate that the universe is fifteen to twenty billion years old, but in view of the ever-increasing possibilities for receiving information from the furthest galaxies yet discovered, it may one day be shown to date from an even earlier period. The universe is said originally to have been formed from a gaseous mass particularly containing hydrogen; it subsequently separated into fragments, thus forming the galaxies. Our own galaxy is probably some ten billion years old. The solar system is likely to have been constituted through a fragmentation of a part of our galaxy. The initial gaseous mass probably evolved to the point where it condensed, and in this way the atoms underwent a transformation : The hydrogen gave rise to helium, then to carbon and oxygen, thus creating various metals and metalloids. The stars also possess a life of their own, causing modern astronomists to classify them according to their stage of evolution. Some stars are now dead and are reduced to the state of extremely compact matter. As matter condensed, so the planets were born. For example, the earth is said to have been formed roughly 4.5 billion years ago. It is highly likely that five billion years from now, the earth will have become a burnt-out celestial body, such as the moon; life will have disappeared from the earth's surface. Specialists in astrophysics regard the existence of multiple worlds as highly likely : They think that stars exist which are at the same stage in evolution as our own sun, and that they are surrounded by certain planets at the same evolutionary stage as the earth. It is not only very logical, but highly probable to suppose that planets similar to our own exist somewhere in the universe.

In *The Bible, the Qur'an and Science,* I noted that statements on a host of subjects are to be found in the Qur'an, among them the following : the Creation in general, which took place in stages, starting from an initially unique mass which subsequently broke into fragments; the plurality of the heavens and the earths; the evolution of the sun and the moon toward an appointed term; and the expansion of the universe. All of these statements are in perfect agreement with data that specialists have either proven or regard as highly probable.

Parallels may clearly be drawn, therefore, between the data of the Scriptures and modern knowledge. The broad outlines of the general evolution of the universe, which may today be deduced from religious teachings when studied as a whole, and from the data of secular knowledge, point toward a steady progression. The latter is gradually moving toward the increased complexity of structures, ranging from the primary nebula to the galaxies, the stars and the planets, with an evolution that ends in death; this has been proven by science in the case of certain very distant celestial bodies, and it is also predicted in the Scriptures with regard to various other bodies which form part of the solar system in which we live.

The evolution of living beings follows the same broad outlines of development toward a larger number of varieties with growing structural complexity–the 'infinity of complexity' mentioned by Father Teilhard de Chardin–, including halts in that evolution, and the disappearance of certain lineages. Since man first appeared on earth, there have been evolutionary changes in his morphology; this evolution is mentioned in the Scriptures and is evident from the vestiges found in ancient terranes. As far as the living world is concerned, the continual enrichment of genetic information has governed all of these transformations : From the bacteria to man, the information has accumulated to a considerable degree within the cell, regulating in the strictest order the changes that have taken place over the course of time.

For the first time in the history of man, notions such as these have come to light. These discoveries are due to the tremendous strides made by science, after moments of hesitation in previous centuries when many theories had subsequently to be replaced by others. Although obscure points still naturally pose difficulties of interpretation, science has today arrived at a stage where certain facts have been firmly established; their basic outlines are not likely to be called into question in the future, even if certain specific aspects of those facts are later clarified.

In every single field, whether the universe, living beings or man, thorough research, performed with no underlying metaphysical intention, clearly shows the existence of an order that is governed by the laws of nature. In the tiniest living organisms that form anatomical and functional units (i.e. the cells), just as in the organisms that possess an even simpler organization, the study of the living world reveals a prodigious structural order which is present right down to the molecular level. The molecule itself, however, composed of a cluster of atoms, is also highly complex. This applies equally to the atom, for physicists have spent decades analysing its 'infinity of complexity' at this infinitely small scale. In view of the above, it is totally illogical to suggest that this favourable organization of structures results from chance, or that, in the case of living organisms which have evolved, the constant accumulation of information responsible for new structures stems from necessity or natural selection *à la* Darwin–even when the latter has been updated through the skillful arguments of the neo-Darwinians. When faced with the inability of science to explain the origin of the prodigious organization of living beings, ranging from the infinitely small to the infinitely large, it is difficult not to turn toward notions of a different order, for it is the material data themselves which suggest this.

To return to the question of man and his origins, we may perhaps formulate the following reply :

There is absolutely no scientific proof to suggest that man was born of the evolved forms of present-day apes. On the contrary, everything argues against this outmoded theory. What science has shown is that, at a certain point in time, a human species appeared which gradually transformed itself into today's man. From a scientific point of view, the crux of the problem is that we do not know what man evolved from : Was it from an autonomous lineage or from one that could be connected with another animal lineage? Whatever the answer, recent studies in genetics indicate that the process could not have taken place by any other method than the addition of new information governing the appearance of structures and functions specific to man. These phenomena fit perfectly into the pattern of an expanding genetic code, as suggested by the theory of creative evolution.

Science does not supply indisputable indications as to the actual moment that the transformation took place, nor on the initial matter employed in the process : Many of the ways in which the change occurred remain a mystery to us. What we can say is that a *new life form* resulted from it, which, as we have already seen, was different from the forms that most closely resemble man from a morphological and functional point of view. This is the very concept of the creation of man by God which appears in general terms in the Scriptures of the three monotheistic religions. It is in absolute harmony with the ideas that may be formed from the firmly established data of science.

Each and every one of these new ideas leads to a comparison between scientific fact and religious teaching, thus causing some of today's philosophers to examine the question in much greater depth :

This may at least be said of those–rare–thinkers who have had the great sense to compare abstract data with the ever–increasing fund of established facts revealed by the development of natural studies.

For example, in 'Problèmes du Christianisme' [*Problems of Christianity*] [1], Claude Tresmontant is clearly aware of the fascination exercised on the scientist by the study of cosmic phenomena, and indeed of biological phenomena, both of which give rise to reflections on the ideas suggested to the philosopher by secular investigations in this field :

"By exploring cosmic, physical and biological creation, the experimental sciences are in fact examining the idea that lies behind God's creation. When all is said and done, it is His creative idea which these sciences attempt to understand, and it is this that fascinates the scientist–as is so often the case–whether he realizes it or not, and regardless of whether he is a monotheist, materialist or monist. By studying the universe, matter or living beings, what the scientist is ultimately trying to understand is a thought–a 'guiding idea', as Claude Bernard would have phrased it; that is why experimental science is usually the first step toward the contemplative life."

This idealistic vision suggested by Claude Tresmontant does not yet seem to have convinced very many specialists in the experimental sciences. Let us hope, at least, that if researchers become better informed on the various religions, they may one day discover a certain harmony between religious teachings and scientific knowledge–or failing this, a compatibility.

1. Published by Editions du Seuil, Paris, 1980.

THE COMPATIBILITY BETWEEN
RELIGION AND SCIENCE

The ideas that have been put forward in the present work have taken us a long way from the concepts that held sway over many of the scientists and philosophers of the last century who regarded religion and science as opposites. Religion was indeed essentially considered to proceed from belief, with its accompanying element of mystery, while science was deemed to be based on reason, for only those facts that could be proven by science were acknowledged as true. Today, however, it is strictly scientific data, which, when applied to an examination of the Holy Scriptures, reveal that religion may be viewed in a light that is different from a pure and simple belief that leaves no room for reason. At the same time however, science is progressing in leaps and bounds, accumulating ever more varied and complex findings, and thereby giving rise to a growing number of genuine enigmas. The fact is, science alone seems incapable of providing answers to some of the questions it raises : We have seen this already in the case of the origin of the genetic code and the accumulation of the information it contains, a phenomenon that has been constant over the course of time. All of the above seems self-evident when it comes to a detailed study of the kind of question raised by the present book, but suitable methods of analysis must be used, allowing for investigations concerning the Holy Scriptures as well as the data of science.

In spite of this, the various judgements that have been made on the general subject of the compatibility between religion and science are often corrupted by serious errors arising from the very manner in which the problem is approached. There are far too many researchers who give priority to metaphysical conceptions rather than to facts. While claiming to take account of material data, such people completely disregard the latter, and base their pronouncements on mainly abstract criteria. The preconceived ideas held by some researchers with regard to one or more of the religions make it very difficult to correct mistaken opinions, especially when these result from the existence of inaccurate texts or mistranslations–a phenomenon I have often noticed. Added to this is the fact that, in some instances, it is very difficult to deal with certain scientific questions– even when expressed very clearly–without employing technical terminology that is hard to grasp. Brilliant minds have been known to lose touch with concrete reality : Their works bear the hallmark of an exclusive predilection for abstraction. It is very rare to find philosophers who support their theories with reflections on subjects other than those belonging to their own field. One must indeed concede that it is extremely difficult for many people to understand data so far out of their normal range of interest, but when they deal with subjects that rely on concrete facts, these commentators must yield to the requirements of material investigation, otherwise their judgements will be unsound.

Preconceived ideas on the religions in general might suggest that those who claim to belong to a religious community would not be able to express themselves in any other way than according to a simple belief. Naturally enough, they can produce no scientific evidence to support their opinions. It therefore follows that such people cannot fail to think that, as far as the religions are concerned, there can be no statements open to human judgement based on logic. After writing *The Bible, the Qur'an and Science,* I often heard it said that the only way of explaining certain passages in the Scriptures that referred to data discovered centuries later by man, was by ascribing their presence to chance. This argument was employed, even though the large number of statements dealing with a wide variety of subjects of this kind quite obviously ruled out any such explanation. Thus, the statement is not actually denied, but any serious study is undercut by simple reference to 'fortuitous accidents', a phrase we have already heard in explanation of the origins of life. In actual fact, the scientific enigma posed by the latter leaves many researchers at a loss for words.

There is no excuse for the fact that contemporary commentators have chosen to ignore a subject on which they nevertheless consider themselves authorized to speak, basing their opinions on data which have only become known over the last few decades. There are good reasons, however, why earlier thinkers put forward inaccurate opinions : They could not possibly have possessed the material data needed to form a correct interpretation at the time they lived. It is always a risky undertaking to try and imagine what certain people of long ago would say today, if we could bring them back to life. I shall therefore limit myself to a single question concerning Renan, a nineteenth-century thinker who could not possibily have had access to present-day knowledge concerning the Scriptures and science. In 1849, Renan wrote 'L'Avenir de la Science' *[The Future of Science]*, which was not published until 1890, and in 1863, he wrote his famous letter to Berthelot, in which he set forth his concept of 'God', a concept which evolved according to the progress of humanity. Now the question at issue is whether or not Renan would have expressed the same ideas, if he had had access to today's discoveries in genetics, molecular biology and the organization of the human cell, and had admitted the existence of enigmas raised by these findings. One wonders whether Renan would have held the same attitude toward the religions, if he had been aware of recent discoveries concerning the history of the monotheistic religions, for they are findings which cast new light on the contents of their respective Scriptures. By the same token, it is debatable whether Darwin, in *On the Origin of Species*, would have championed the same ideas, had he possessed access to modern data concerning the genes : My guess is that these two researchers would indeed have expressed themselves differently. It is staggering to think how few scientific data they had at their disposal to support their final conclusions, compared with the immense fund of knowledge on the same subjects which we now hold at our command! As we celebrate the centenary of the birth of Father Teilhard de Chardin, I cannot help wondering whether the conclusions he drew would not have contained even more convincing arguments, were he alive today. One wonders whether he would have taken account of today's realistic concepts concerning the origin of the Biblical texts, which have been duly acknowledged, and also of the firmly established discoveries that have been made over the last decades in the fields of genetics and molecular biology. As far as I am concerned, this 'aristocrat of the intelligence'–to quote the phrase coined by the French President during a celebratory eulogy at Unesco–would indeed have made use of these new data.

Although scientific materialism boasts of its triumphs, we are perhaps about to witness a reversal of ideas that in the West is totally unexpected, for it has mainly been caused by strictly materialistic data. In spite of what one might say, scientific knowledge does indeed seem to lead to reflections on the existence of God. The prodigious organization presiding over the birth and perpetuation of life; an evolution that is governed by the accumulation of new information recorded in the genes; the evolution of the universe within which these events take place–all of these factors argue strongly in favour of a methodical organization of phenomena that developed in perfect order.

In this context, the basic compatibility between religion and science emerges very plainly. Although for many centuries difficulties existed for Christians, due to the presence of scientific errors in the Bible, modern explanations have dispelled this profound uneasiness, for they are based on the conclusions that arise from detailed study of the texts. The declaration issued by the Second Vatican Council (1962-1965) acknowledges that the Books of the Old Testament may contain material that is 'imperfect and obsolete'. From a Christian point of view, this admission has–or certainly ought to have–put a stop to a problem that has persisted since the seventeenth century. Fifteen centuries before the Council, however, Saint Augustine–who naturally thought that God could not possibly impart to man ideas that did not correspond to reality–was perfectly willing to banish from the sacred text any statement that he considered worthy of exclusion for this reason. The controversy that raged during the last century between those who upheld the fixity of species as stated in the Bible, and those who opposed it, might have turned out very differently indeed, if the Christian authorities had earlier admitted the existence of scientific errors in the Bible–'the errors of mankind, for long ago man was like a child, as yet ignorant of science", to repeat J. Guitton's phrase. In such circumstances, the objections to the far-fetched theories of Darwin's followers concerning the supposed simian origins of man might well have been countered by more solidly based arguments. Instead, however, Darwin's opponents doggedly defended the fixity of species as presented in the Bible, refusing to consider any other way of approaching the texts. As a result, they lost the battle before it had even started [1].

It should be noted that this was not the situation in the Muslim world. At a time when Western science, though still in its infancy, was already at odds with religion, such controversies did not exist in Islam. The reasons for this lie deep in Islamic history–at its very origins in fact. A Muslim tradition dates back to this period, according to which the increase of knowledge must always be encouraged. The Prophet indeed ordered the believers to : "Search for science from the cradle to the grave", "search for science, even in China", by which he meant that no journey could be too long, if it

---

1. Without the above decision of the Second Vatican Council, critical studies of the Bible would probably still suffer from the kind of ostracism that greeted Darwin's theories.

served this purpose. Many verses in the Qur'an urge man to seek for signs of God's omnipotence through his contemplation of natural phenomena of all kinds. It is no exaggeration to state that this early command of nascent Islam to cultivate science, was the religious driving force behind the blossoming of Islamic civilization, which flourished in the Middle Ages and from which Europe reaped such tremendous cultural benefits.

Along with recent discoveries concerning one of the aspects of the general relationship between science and religion, this reminder of events from the distant past should help bring together the points of view of the members of each religious community who all believe in the same God, just as other questions from other fields should help create points in common between them. Although the terms in which the idea was expressed may have changed over the course of time, the Scriptures nevertheless remind all believers that they share a single God. Throughout the present study, emphasis has been laid on the fact that the concept of a Creation was not at all incompatible with the latest scientific data. Morevoer, it has been repeatedly stressed that the process of Creation must logically have taken place over the course of time through the increase in genetic information, which would appear to be the necessary explanation of the transformations undergone by living beings.

It is therefore somewhat easier today to reply to the question : "What is the Origin of Man?" In order to arrive at this, however, we have had to proceed to a scrupulously objective analysis of science and the Scriptures of the monotheistic religions. Along the way, we have encountered some surprising ideas : for example, the discovery of certain texts which have traditionally been considered definitive and which have recently been proclaimed partly 'obsolete'. At the same time, we have seen that the progress of science and the increase in our knowledge of the history of science make it quite impossible for certain other sacred texts to be of human origin. This is indeed a dramatic change in our approach to an examination of the Holy Scriptures! It is particularly overwhelming for people in the West, who often know very little indeed about religions that are not common to their part of the world, and who are often provided with irrational, sentimental arguments that have no place in a study of such questions. We can only hope that these misguided attitudes will henceforth cease to interfere with the analysis of the subjects that appear in all three of the monotheistic religions and which form the theme of the present work. If these attitudes are abandoned, then men of goodwill can approach the question from the point of view recommended by the Second Vatican Council :

"Today as never before perhaps, thanks to God, there is a clear possibility of profound agreement between true science and true faith, both of which are servants of the one and only truth."

In the present comparison between religious teachings and scientific data, a compatibility has indeed emerged which strongly contrasts with the passionate controversies of the past. It indicates that the investigation of a subject such as the one studied in this book becomes much clearer when people set aside ideological hypotheses and, as their sole criteria, rely on established facts, logical deduction and the power of reason.

INDEX OF QUOTATIONS
FROM THE QUR'AN

ACHEVÉ D'IMPRIMER
LE 19 DÉCEMBRE 1984
SUR LES PRESSES DE
L'IMPRIMERIE HÉRISSEY
À ÉVREUX (EURE)

Imprimé en France
N° d'éditeur : L 237
N° d'imprimeur : 36146
Dépôt légal : novembre 1982